LILAC MILLS

A Stitch in Time in Applewell

CANELO

First published in the United Kingdom in 2022 by

Canelo
Unit 9, 5th Floor
Cargo Works, 1–2 Hatfields
London, SE1 9PG
United Kingdom

A CIP catalogue record for this book is available from the British Library.

Print ISBN 978 1 80032 318 6
Ebook ISBN 978 1 80032 317 9

Look for more great books at www.canelo.co

Printed and bound in Great Britain by Clays Ltd, Elcograf S.p.A.

1

A Stitch in Time in Applewell

Lilac Mills lives on a Welsh mountain with her very patient husband and incredibly sweet dog, where she grows veggies (if the slugs don't get them), bakes (badly) and loves making things out of glitter and glue (a mess, usually). She's been an avid reader ever since she got her hands on a copy of *Noddy Goes to Toytown* when she was five, and she once tried to read everything in her local library starting with A and working her way through the alphabet. She loves long, hot summer days and cold winter ones snuggled in front of the fire, but whatever the weather she's usually writing or thinking about writing, with heartwarming romance and happy-ever-afters always on her mind.

Also by Lilac Mills

A Very Lucky Christmas
Sunshine at Cherry Tree Farm
Summer on the Turquoise Coast
Love in the City by the Sea

Tanglewood Village series

The Tanglewood Tea Shop
The Tanglewood Flower Shop
The Tanglewood Wedding Shop

Island Romance

Sunrise on the Coast
Holiday in the Hills
Sunset on the Square

Applewell Village

Waste Not, Want Not in Applewell
Make Do and Mend in Applewell
A Stitch in Time in Applewell

Chapter 1

Lucas

A familiar and unwelcome dread rose in Lucas Grainger's chest as he drove past the sign for Applewell. Once upon a time he couldn't wait to leave, and here he was seventeen years later returning to it. About time too, Effron would have said, had he still been alive.

It was Effron who had made him promise to come back, but Lucas wasn't entirely sure that keeping a promise was the only reason why he was returning – because, let's face it, where else could he go? And not only that, he had long-overdue bridges to mend.

Although the village was two miles from the coast, Lucas could smell the salty tang of the Irish Sea as he wound his window down and he breathed deeply, welcoming the fresh clean smells flooding into the car – a far cry from the city air he'd left behind. Set in rolling Welsh hills and surrounded by farmland, Applewell hadn't changed. But then, he hadn't expected it to, and that sameness was part of the reason he'd left in the first place. He'd just gone about his escape the wrong way, that was all, and he'd hurt his family badly in the process. Lucas didn't think he'd ever be able to forgive himself for that, and guilt rode him hard.

As he entered the outskirts and headed for his mother's house in the heart of the village, he thought about the small, terraced cottage he'd grown up in, and—

Dear God!

Lucas slammed on the brakes and his car skidded to a halt.

A banner hung from the bedroom windows, stretched across the front of the house for all to see.

WELCOME HOME

It reminded him of some show he'd seen on TV. The man in it had just been released from prison...

His mother was waiting for him on the front step. So were most of the street's inhabitants.

Lucas's gaze slid past her and came to rest on his sister. Their eyes met and she nodded, a tiny movement of her head. The little girl she was holding stared openly at him, appearing to be on the brink of tears, and he didn't blame her: he felt like crying himself.

So much for slipping back unnoticed.

He'd prepared himself for the nosiness of the villagers, for their well-meaning stares and comments, but *this*? His mother was throwing him a damned party, and Lucas's instinct was to turn the car around and drive hell for leather back to London.

Instead, he put it into first gear and trundled slowly up the road, pulling in when he found a parking space.

He got out slowly and stretched, easing the kinks out of his back from the five-hour journey, trying to buy himself some time.

It was no use.

With a shriek his mum was upon him, her arms grappling him into a hug. He could feel her trembling as she rose on tiptoe to shower his cheeks in kisses.

'Lucas, my Lucas!' she cried. 'You're home.'

'Not for good, Mum,' he warned.

She leant back, her eyes scanning his face. 'It's good enough for me.'

'I'm not staying.' He felt the need to repeat it, the banner unnerving him. He didn't want her to think this was a permanent move. 'I *will* be going back to London.' He had to – his life was there, not here. But in the meantime, this was home.

Her face crumpled. 'I know. But you're here now and that's what matters.'

She hugged him again, her embrace fierce, as though now she'd got him home she would never let him go.

Home. Such an evocative word. He hadn't thought of Applewell as home for a very long time.

Liar, his conscience whispered. He ignored it.

Eventually his mother pulled away, although she kept one arm tight around his waist as she dragged him towards the crowd gathered outside the house. Eleven people were watching the return of the prodigal son. He imagined that their smiles and nods, and the pats on the back they gave him as his mother led him towards the front door, hid the belief that they knew he'd come back one day. That he wouldn't be able to stay away.

He hated that they were right. Applewell had been calling him back for half of his life, and he'd finally given in.

'Nora.' He halted when he reached his sister.

'Lucas.' Her expression was neutral and he wondered how she felt about him being here. She tilted her head to the child in her arms. 'You remember Ruby.'

How could he forget his niece? 'She's grown.'

'Children have a habit of doing that.'

Was that a tinge of disapproval in her voice? If it was, he didn't blame her – he'd only seen his niece twice since she'd been born and the little girl must be close to three. Lucas had a panicked thought – had he missed her birthday? No, he couldn't have. She'd been born in June.

The child hid her face in her mother's shoulder until all he could see was a plump cheek, the hint of a rosebud mouth with a thumb in it, and the sweep of long dark lashes.

He resisted the urge to stroke her soft skin. He didn't have the right. Not yet. Ruby didn't know him, but he intended to rectify that. One of the things he was looking forward to was getting to know his niece. And his sister – if she'd let him.

'Come inside,' his mother urged, pushing him through the front door. 'I've put on a little spread. You must be hungry.'

Despite not having eaten a thing today, Lucas didn't have any appetite. Nausea had been his companion on the journey, and stopping three times on the way for double shots of coffee hadn't helped his roiling stomach.

He came to a halt in the living room, seeing the dining table laden with buffet food.

'I didn't know what you'd like, so I've done a bit of everything.' She walked past and picked up a plate, hesitantly holding it out to him.

'Do you mind if I freshen up first?' he asked, conscious of people crowding in behind him.

'Of course not. Sorry, I should have thought...'

'I just need to wash my hands.' Lucas held them up as though there were layers of dirt on them.

'It's through there.' His mum pointed towards the kitchen and the downstairs loo beyond, then immediately bit her lip. 'Silly me, you know where it is.'

Lucas would have preferred the relative seclusion of the upstairs bathroom but any respite would do for now, so he hurried through the kitchen and into the tiny lobby beyond, with the cloakroom to the right and the door to the back garden straight ahead. It briefly registered that she'd had the small outside space landscaped since the last time he'd been here, then he slipped into the loo and shut the door.

Lucas leant against it, taking deep breaths.

Damn, this was difficult.

He'd kind of been expecting it – not the party, obviously, but the awkwardness, the feeling of being a guest, a stranger almost. It would take them both a while to stop tiptoeing around each other, although he didn't think for one minute that he and his mum would slip back into the routines and patterns of his youth.

How could they, given that his youth had long disappeared? He'd taken it to London with him and left it there. He'd been a grown man the first time he'd ventured back to Applewell after he'd run away, and far older in experience than his age had warranted.

Lucas washed his hands and splashed water on his face, avoiding looking at his reflection, fearing what he might see in his eyes. Then, having run out of excuses, he went back into the fray.

'He's a bomper of a bloke, your Lucas,' an elderly woman was saying. He vaguely remembered her as living two doors down.

'Bomper' – he hadn't heard that word in a while. But the woman was right: Lucas was the first to admit he was a big man. Regular workouts in the gym had given his shoulders and chest added depth. Combined with running, the exercise served to keep his waist trim and his legs firm.

Being tall and well-built had been an advantage on the streets.

'He looks well, mind you,' someone else said, and yet another added, 'You must be pleased to have him back.'

He couldn't see his mother's face but he could tell from the way she held herself that she was finding the situation difficult, and Lucas wondered if he should intervene and ask everyone to leave.

However, this wasn't his house, these people weren't his neighbours, and he didn't live in this village.

With sudden clarity he understood why his mother had made a fuss: she wanted to tell the world that she wasn't ashamed of him. And he also realised she must have been very ashamed (and hurt) when he'd run away. This celebration of his return was Vivien's way of telling Applewell she had a son to be proud of.

It had been a long time coming.

'Here he is!' Donald Mousel slapped Lucas on the back. 'Welcome home, boy.'

'Hello, Donald. How are you?' When had the man become so old? He was old when Lucas left, but anyone over twenty-five looked old to a seventeen-year-old. Donald really was old now and Lucas guessed he must be in his late sixties, early seventies.

He almost chuckled — if Effron could hear him refer to someone in their seventies as old, he would have given Lucas an earbashing. Lucas guessed Effron had been born old and had just carried on with it for the rest of his life. Ageless and unageing, that's how Effron had seemed, right up until the end when he'd gone downhill fast and had collapsed in on himself like a black hole. He'd always loved space and the universe, had Effron, so the analogy was particularly apt. Lucas blinked back sudden tears. God, he missed him! The man had been more of a father to him than his real dad had. Lucas would never have survived those first fraught and terrifying weeks on the streets if Effron, who had been homeless since he was a young man himself, hadn't taken him under his wing. Lucas owed him his life and his sanity.

'Bet you're glad to be back,' Donald said. He was holding a paper plate piled high with food.

Lucas didn't feel glad. What he felt was resigned, guilty, ashamed, apprehensive… But that was his cross to bear and he had no intention of sharing his feelings. He'd become very adept at hiding them over the years, so he nodded and smiled politely, then moved away.

He didn't get far.

It seemed like most of Applewell wanted to have a few words with him, many along the lines of how pleased they were to see him, how happy his mother must be to have him back, and how he'd soon feel as though he'd never been away.

Out of all the comments it was that last one which made him feel the worst. Why did they think he'd left in the first place?

Actually, now that he came to think of it, why *did* they think he'd left? What rumours had gone around? What speculation had the villagers whispered behind cupped hands whilst giving his mother sympathetic looks? Even though he'd phoned to tell her he was safe and had continued to call her on a regular basis (he hadn't been a *total* shit), the villagers must have gossiped and wondered.

He had no doubt, though, that Applewell's sympathy for Vivien had been genuine and they would have rallied around and supported her as best they could. They were good like that, but that was also one of the reasons he had felt he couldn't stay – everyone knowing everyone else's business, nothing to do, no excitement… no future.

He'd fled to the exact opposite. Anonymous, no one giving a fig, plenty of excitement. Sometimes more than he'd been able to handle.

Yes, he'd carved a future for himself, despite living on the streets for the first few years, but the question now was, did he still want that future?

And this was why he was here in Applewell, back in his old room, in the bosom of his family and the oh-so familiar arms of the village he'd run away from as soon as he'd been able to.

Chapter 2

Gracie

I should learn to cook, Gracie Stewart thought to herself, as she did every time she walked into Eleri Jones's cafe. But if she was honest, she couldn't be bothered. She much preferred to spend her time with a sewing needle in her hand, rather than a wooden spoon. It might cost her more to eat out every day, but with only herself to cater for there didn't seem much point in going to all the effort. Besides, she welcomed the break from work.

'What's on the specials board?' Gracie asked, as she did every day, despite it being written in white chalk on the board behind the counter.

'Creamy chicken pesto pasta.' Eleri looked up from making patterns in the top of a cup of coffee. 'How are you? You're late today.'

She was very late indeed. Gracie normally took her lunch between one and two in the afternoon, but it was nearly four o'clock and this meal was now more like dinner. No wonder her tummy had been rumbling. 'I've been making coasters and placemats for a wedding, and I wanted to finish the last one before I took a break. The bride wanted everything to match, and because there were loads of scraps left over from when she had the bridesmaids' dresses altered, she asked if I could do something with them for the table.'

'You sound busy.'

'I am.' Gracie beamed. It had been a gamble opening the shop, not only financially but also emotionally. So far it was

8

paying off, despite her terrible shyness and her fear of meeting new people. When she'd been working out of her tiny front room she hadn't had the general public wandering in, but she'd felt it was the right decision to open A Stitch in Time and so far she hadn't regretted it. 'I quite fancy the pasta. Is there any left?' she asked.

'I thought you might, so I kept a portion back for you. Sit down and I'll bring it over. Water or orange juice?'

'Water today, please.'

Gracie took a seat near the window and gazed out at the street. She had a similar view from the window of her own shop and she often sat near it to sew. The light was better there, and she enjoyed watching people as they went about their business.

Gracie waved to Tony, the owner of Pins to Elephants, as he popped next door into the grocers, and she pulled a face at little Morgan Hargreaves who was out with his mum. The small boy stuck his tongue out and Gracie giggled. She shouldn't encourage him, but he was so cute and such a dynamo – he kept his mum, Lottie, on her toes, that's for sure.

'Heard the news?' Eleri asked, placing a piping hot dish in front of Gracie and handing her some cutlery wrapped in a serviette.

'No, what?' Gracie unwrapped her knife and fork and placed the napkin on her lap.

'Lucas Grainger is back in town.'

'Who?'

'Vivien's son.'

'I'd forgotten she had a son,' Gracie said, tucking into her meal.

Eleri pulled out a chair and sank down into it. If the cafe wasn't too busy, Eleri often kept her company. 'You must remember him – he ran away when he was about seventeen. It was the talk of Applewell.'

Gracie shrugged, her mouth full. She chewed and swallowed, a memory slowly filtering to the surface. 'Vaguely. I was about eleven, I think. I didn't take much notice, to be honest. Knowing me, I was probably too busy with those dance classes I used to go to. I was obsessed with them. Pity I had two left feet.' Gracie sighed wistfully. Her childhood dream had been to become a famous dancer. Before that, she'd wanted to be a cowboy. Instead, she'd become a seamstress.

'Anyway, he's back. Vivien is throwing him a party as we speak.'

'Why did he run away?'

Eleri pulled a face. 'No idea. There were rumours, of course, some of them unsavoury, but his mother always insisted he was a good kid and wasn't in any trouble. He's done well for himself, though,' she added. 'Works for some charity. UnderCover, I think, although I might be wrong.'

'I wonder if Catrin knows him?'

'She might do. I'll have to ask her.'

'I'm going over there after this, so I can ask her if you like and report back tomorrow.' Although Applewell had an influx of visitors every season, the villagers didn't take a great deal of interest in them, but when something happened concerning one of their own they rallied around like buffalo defending their young against a lion. Outsiders might call it nosiness or being busybodies, but Gracie knew it was Applewell's community spirit. They looked out for one another, and the more that was known about a situation, the better placed they were to help – if help was what was needed.

For some reason Gracie suspected that it would be, but she wasn't sure whether it would be Vivien who'd need the help, or Catrin.

–

'Have you heard the news?' Catrin demanded the second Gracie stepped through UnderCover's door.

'About Vivien's son? Yes, I have.'

'You know he works for UnderCover?'

'Eleri said he might, but she wasn't entirely sure.'

'I've had an email from head office in London. They want me to "afford him all the help necessary". Their words, not mine. It would have been nice if they'd told me what help would be needed. And why.' Catrin bit her lip, her brow creased into a frown.

Gracie had rarely seen her friend with anything other than a smile on her face. Catrin was the sunniest person she knew.

'I wonder what that means?' Gracie mused.

'You and me both.' Catrin wrinkled her nose. 'Do you think they sent him to spy on me?'

'I doubt it; they wouldn't have announced it if they had.'

'True. But what help am I supposed to be affording him?' Catrin's eyes widened. 'Do you think they're going to sack me?'

'Why would they do that? You've managed this shop for years and you're good at it.'

'What if they want to sell up? The premises must be worth a fair bit.'

'What would be the point? They'd only have to buy or rent somewhere else.'

'Not if they are planning on closing it down completely.'

'Again, why would they do that? The shop's doing OK, isn't it?'

Catrin nodded, but she continued to worry at her lip. Gracie felt for her friend. Catrin had worked for UnderCover for years – she was the only paid employee in the shop, the rest being volunteers. She loved working there, and although Gracie knew Catrin would be able to quickly find another job should her fears be realised, it wasn't the point.

'It'll be fine,' Gracie said, crossing her fingers and praying that was the case. 'I'm sure there's a simple explanation. He's probably only here for a flying visit to see his mother.'

'Then why the email? And Vivien has put up a welcome home banner. Would she do that if he was only here for a few days?'

Gracie didn't have an answer. All she could do was to repeat what she'd just said. 'I'm sure there's a logical explanation.'

'Yeah, that they're closing UnderCover down and I'll be out of a job.' Catrin looked positively morose.

Gracie wished she could do more to reassure her. 'I'm sure they're not,' was all she could say.

'I've got a bag of oddments for you,' Catrin said. 'It's out the back. I won't be a tick.'

Gracie moved over to a rack of dresses while she waited, and felt the fabric of one of them. It was brocade: a richer and heavier fabric than was normal for modern clothes, and the design was the middle of the last century. It was a vintage piece and was priced accordingly, although, in a shop in London, it would fetch three or four times the asking price.

She was still studying it when the shop door opened and a man came in. He was a stranger and she assumed he was a tourist.

'Catrin, you've got a customer,' she called. 'Catrin's the manager. She won't be long; she's just popped out the back,' she said to the man.

He nodded once, but his attention was on the racks and shelves as he scanned the contents, and he didn't look at her. Gracie looked at him though, and it wasn't solely to make sure he didn't steal anything. He was taller than average, wide-shouldered, and with the sort of face that could get a woman into trouble. Dark-haired, blue-eyed, chisel-jawed trouble.

Oops! He'd caught her staring and Gracie hastily looked away.

'Good afternoon,' Catrin trilled, spotting him as she came back onto the shop floor. She was carrying a large bag which she handed to Gracie and said, 'I won't say I hope you find some use for it, because I know you will.' She turned to the man. 'Can I help you with anything, or are you just looking?'

'I'm just looking – for the moment,' he said.

Gracie blushed, because what he was looking at was her, and his scrutiny was unsettling. Men didn't often look at her like they wanted to eat her up and spit out her bones. They didn't look at her at all. It sent a quiver right through her, and she was glad to leave.

'Thanks, Catrin. We'll catch up later when you know a bit more. Try not to worry, eh?' she said, heading for the door.

'I'll try.'

'Fancy going to The Busy Bumble on Friday evening? We can have a proper chinwag,' Gracie asked as she was about to slip outside.

'Sounds good to me. I'll check with Gareth and get back to you.' Despite Catrin's smile, Gracie could tell that she was going to worry like crazy and she hoped her friend would find out what was going on soon.

Putting her own worries aside, Gracie trotted back to her shop, eager to sort through the bag of goodies Catrin had given her. Deciding what she could use other people's cast-offs for was one of the favourite parts of her job.

Chapter 3

Lucas

What the hell had he just witnessed? Lucas asked himself, as he watched the woman leave the shop carrying a large bag. He'd not seen any money change hands, so he was pretty sure the items in that bag hadn't been paid for.

However, he didn't want to get off on the wrong foot with Catrin. At least the woman who'd just left had done him a favour by calling the one now standing in front of him by name, so he knew he was looking at Catrin Williams, who, according to his records, managed this particular branch of UnderCover and so wasn't one of the volunteers.

He wasn't happy that Catrin had left the shop floor unattended either, but that was also a conversation for another time.

Or maybe she hadn't, he thought, hastily reassessing the situation. The woman who'd left might have been a volunteer. It was best he checked the lay of the land before jumping to any conclusions. If she was a volunteer, he'd probably get to meet her at some point, although in a small place like Applewell he'd likely meet her sooner rather than later anyway. Who was she, he mused, wondering if she had been in school with him – albeit several years below him, as he guessed her to be closer to Nora's age than to his own.

'See anything you like?' Catrin asked. She was wearing a professional smile.

'Hmm,' he said, pushing the woman's face out of his mind and gathering his thoughts. He stepped towards the shop's manager and held out a hand. 'I'm Lucas Grainger and you must be Catrin Williams. You should have received an email about me.'

Catrin shook his hand and wore a polite smile on her lips, but she looked concerned. 'Oh, um, nice to meet you.'

'Did they tell you why I'm here?'

'No...'

Lucas was relieved that Jonas, his boss, was letting him sort out his own cover story. Although it wasn't technically a story – he really *did* want to explore how the shops could be improved at the grass roots level, and this was an ideal opportunity.

The charity employed several area managers who oversaw the smooth running of their patch, but they were only concerned with the day-to-day operation of them, not overall strategy or the bigger picture. Lucas was aiming to think outside the box. Even though the shops were mostly manned by a whole raft of wonderful volunteers, they still cost money to run, which ate into the funds available to provide shelter and food for those people who truly mattered – the homeless.

'I don't want to get under your feet, and I'm not here to interfere. I just want to understand what it is you do,' he explained.

Catrin was staring at him, her expression unfathomable. 'We get donations from the public and we sell as many of those items as we can for as much as we can,' she said slowly.

He realised he hadn't expressed himself clearly. 'Sorry, you must think I'm an idiot. I'm hoping to gain some insight into how we can streamline things to maximise profits for the organisation. Anyway,' he continued when she didn't answer, 'I'll have a quick look around and then I'll leave you to get on with things. I'm sure you've got plenty to do.'

Lucas wandered around the shop, examining the goods on sale and looking at price tags. The charity had set amounts that should be charged for particular items, but there was some discretion given to each store manager because not all items were of the same quality or in the same condition, and some makes were more popular than others and could fetch higher prices.

As well as clothes, the charity was also happy to receive bric-a-brac, furniture, china – in fact, anything that people wanted to donate. Within reason, of course.

UnderCover also had its own range of greeting cards, key rings, and other assorted things that were small, cheap to manufacture, yet kept the charity in people's minds.

Toys were another favourite, and he stopped to admire the display of cuddly animals. Lucas had never been a fan of lumping them all in a tub for customers to rummage through, and he was particularly pleased to see them on a shelf, bears grouped together with other bears, bunnies with other bunnies, and so on, and there was also a rather appealing range of colourful rag dolls.

He picked one up, feeling its squashy body and admiring the bright colours. The price it was on sale for was reasonable, and all the dolls looked brand new.

Lucas put it back and moved on to the household section. The things that people donated never failed to amaze him. Here was a perfectly good dinner service with all the pieces. It even had a sauce boat, and although the pattern was slightly dated it was a lovely set.

His eyes roamed around the walls and came to rest on a picture of a flamenco dancer around a campfire at night. He'd lost count of the number of times he'd seen this image or one very much like it – they must have been manufactured in their thousands back in the day. He shook his head, smiling at it.

'That, along with loads of other stuff, came from a hotel in Danyravon. I've still got tonnes of things out the back from them,' Catrin said. 'That picture is a throwback to the Seventies, isn't it? I actually quite like it.'

'So do I,' Lucas admitted. 'I'm not too keen on the frame, though.'

They stood side by side, gazing at it for a moment, then Lucas gave himself a shake. He'd told his mum he wouldn't be long, so he'd better get back.

After the initial fuss and flurry earlier, and once everyone had eaten their fill, Vivien's friends and neighbours had drifted away, leaving him, his mother, his sister and niece alone in the house. Lucas had taken his bags upstairs to his old room. When he'd paid his first fleeting visit to Applewell several years after running away, he'd been relieved to see that his old room had been stripped of anything remotely reminiscent of his boyhood (his mother hadn't kept it as a shrine to him, thank goodness).

After he'd unpacked, he'd come back downstairs and said he needed to stretch his legs. It was partly true. After such a long drive he had been feeling stiff, but he'd also wanted to get out of the house for a while. How on earth he was going to spend the next few weeks here, he had no idea. His mum was doing her best to make him feel at home and he admired her spirit in announcing to the whole village that she was pleased to have him back, even if it wasn't on a permanent basis. She'd refused to allow him to slink back to Applewell with his tail between his legs, but it was all a bit much right now. He was feeling rather weird, as though an older, stranger version of himself was being superimposed on the teenage boy he'd once been. Oddly, Lucas felt as though he'd been fast-forwarded in time, and had skipped all the intervening years since he'd left.

Abruptly he came out of his reverie.

'I've seen enough,' he announced, without warning. 'You'll be closing soon, so I'll let you get on with it.'

With that, Lucas marched out of the door and down the street, leaving the manager staring at him with a bewildered expression on her face. Once outside UnderCover though, he slowed to a more reasonable pace, not wanting to draw attention to himself. No doubt he'd receive enough of that in due course.

At first glance, he didn't think Applewell's main street had changed a great deal. The butcher shop was still there, as were the bakers, the grocers, and the store that sold almost anything you could think of, called Pins to Elephants.

He paused when a name above the door of a cafe caught his attention. Well, well, well… Eleri Jones had opened her own place. He remembered her as a kid, a few years older than him, selling cups of homemade lemonade and garishly iced fairy cakes from a makeshift table outside her front door.

He wondered whether she looked the same or whether she had aged as much as he. For a moment, he debated calling in for a coffee but decided against it. The Applewell drums would have told her he was back, so there would be time enough to show his face. The cafe had been there long before Eleri had put her name above the door, and it had always been a hotbed of gossip. He assumed it probably hadn't changed.

Another shop claimed his attention. This one was also new to him. A Stitch in Time it was called, and what made him look at it twice was the woman sitting near the window. Her head was bowed but he could have sworn it was the same person who had been in UnderCover earlier.

He halted, not wanting to stare, and pretended to be fascinated by the notices in the newsagent's window next door (was Sid still running it?). Casually, he looked to his left, and his eyes met a pair of startlingly navy ones. He became dimly aware of creamy skin dotted with freckles and wild nut-brown hair, before he tore his gaze away.

Yep, that was the woman who'd been in UnderCover.

The woman whose face had lingered in his mind for longer than it should have done.

He wouldn't describe her as classically beautiful, but she was arresting with her large, luminous blue eyes and corkscrew hair. A too-wide mouth sat below high cheekbones and above a narrow and delicate chin. She reminded him of a stray kitten that one of his long-ago girlfriends had adopted. From what he remembered, he'd been more attached to the cat than he had been to her. Needless to say, the relationship hadn't lasted.

Fleetingly, he wondered whether this woman, whose gaze he could feel on his retreating back as he did an about turn and headed towards his mother's house, was married.

Then, in an attempt to even things up in his mind, he also wondered if Catrin was married. He'd not noticed a ring; but then again, he hadn't looked for one. And the reason he hadn't looked for one was because he didn't care either way. The manager of Applewell's branch of UnderCover didn't hold any appeal for him in that respect.

The woman in A Stitch in Time, however, did.

Thankful that he wouldn't be here long enough to act on the attraction he felt, he pushed her image out of his mind. He had more important things to think about right now, such as building bridges with his mother and sister, and getting to know his beautiful little niece. A brief fling was definitely not on his radar.

Chapter 4

Gracie

He'd been staring at her, the man who'd been in UnderCover earlier. Gracie had felt eyes on her, weighty and searching, and she'd looked up from what she was doing to find him outside the newsagents staring in. She should have found it disturbing, a man looking at her like that. But she hadn't. She'd found it thrilling.

Ah, well, it had been fun while it lasted, she thought, as he broke eye contact and marched off. Gracie often amused herself by thinking about the people she saw from her window. It wasn't all head-down and needle flying. For the sake of her eyesight and her concentration, she frequently looked up from her work to gaze at the people on the other side of the glass.

Sometimes they gazed back at her, but mostly they were oblivious to her existence, either not noticing her at all, or far too engrossed in her window display to see the figure beyond. She preferred it that way – if they saw something they liked, they might come in and buy it.

Her attention was drawn to Lottie Hargreaves for a second time today. This time the woman was accompanied by her two other children as well as Morgan, and she was heading towards A Stitch in Time.

'I would have called in to Eleri's cafe to speak to you,' Lottie said, as she ushered her brood inside. 'But I didn't have the time. I had to pick these two up from school. Robin had art club and Sabrina had dance. I expect you're about to close.'

'Not yet,' Gracie said. One of the advantages of being your own boss, both in a business and a personal sense, was that she had no one to answer to and no one to rush home for. It was both a blessing and a curse.

She had been sorting through the bag of clothes and fabric that Catrin had given her, working out which things could be salvaged, which items had intact zips that she could reuse, buttons to be snipped off and stored, and whether any fabric could be made into something else. Very little went to waste in A Stitch in Time. Every scrap of material, unless stained or threadbare would have a use, eventually. The task was absorbing (if she ignored male eyes gazing at her through the window) and she didn't want to go home until she'd finished.

'I wondered if you'd give a demonstration in reupholstering,' Lottie asked. 'Many of my students have expressed an interest.'

'Are you trying to put me out of a job?' Gracie teased, tongue-in-cheek.

'No! Sorry, I didn't think.'

'I'm joking – I'd love to. Upholstery isn't really my thing, as you know, but if you think it'll help, why not?'

Lottie beamed at her. The woman had not long started up a business of her own, teaching courses on upcycling furniture, and Gracie was happy to help.

'I'll pay you, of course,' Lottie added.

'I don't want paying – not in the conventional sense.'

'Morgan, please don't touch that.' The little boy was running his hands over the top of Gracie's sewing machine.

'He's fine. It's not plugged in.'

'You'd be surprised what damage this child can do,' Lottie said. 'What do you need?'

'Can you ask Henry to keep a look out for a Welsh dresser? I've got one, but I'd like another. Things sell better when they're displayed nicely.'

Lottie looked at the dresser Gracie already had. 'It's lovely with all that bunting. Very Cath Kidston. Of course I'll ask him. Things like that turn up all the time.'

Henry managed a tip shop in Aberystwyth. He spent his days foraging around in the massive containers in the local household reclamation site, fishing out items that were too good to be scrapped, and sometimes those that weren't. This was where Lottie came in, because she was a dab hand at turning broken pieces of furniture into something new, and now she was teaching other people how to do the same.

Gracie loved bartering for what she wanted, rather than being paid in cash – it was far more fun that way. She'd once made fat cushions for Eleri's cafe in exchange for a week's worth of hot meals, and she thought she'd got the best end of the deal.

That was the nice thing about Applewell – everyone looked out for one another. Talking of which…

'Have you heard that Vivien's son is back in town?' Gracie asked.

'I didn't know she had a son.' Lottie was from North Wales originally and was also about ten years older than her, so it was to be expected that she mightn't have heard of Lucas Grainger.

'I'd forgotten, but Eleri reminded me that he'd run away when he was a teenager. He's back now, and he's going to be around for some time by the sound of it. He works for UnderCover and Catrin is worried he's here to sell the premises or something.'

'I'm sure there's nothing to worry about,' Lottie said.

'I told her the same.'

They chatted for a while longer, before Lottie said, 'Come on, you lot, let's go home. I bet you're starving.' Lottie rounded her children up and shepherded them out of the door, with a promise to Gracie to be in touch when she'd firmed up a date for the demonstration.

Gracie was pleased to be asked, even though she'd not given a demonstration before and the prospect terrified her. However, she welcomed any new string to her bow, no matter how thin; she was constantly aware of her finances, even more so now than when she'd been working out of her tiny front room as she'd done ever since buying a home of her own. She said 'buying' but the vast majority of it was owned by the mortgage company, and she was always extremely conscious that she had the mortgage to pay, as well as the rest of her bills.

Over the past couple of years, her little sewing business had gone from strength to strength, so a few months ago she'd taken her courage in both hands and had made the huge decision to rent a small shop on the high street. It had been possibly the scariest thing she'd ever done, and not just because of the financial commitment. Running the shop meant dealing with total strangers every single day. It was bad enough dealing with people she knew... But her one consolation and the driving force behind her incredibly brave decision to open a shop, was her complete and utter certainty that she was good at what she did. It wasn't blowing her own trumpet to admit that she was an excellent seamstress and tailor, and seeing the delight on her customers' faces and hearing the compliments they paid her almost made up for having to talk to them. Also, it helped that she could lose herself in the safe world of mending and sewing in between customers, so she didn't become too overwhelmed.

It was still early days for her business though, and she relied heavily on Catrin giving her fabric and unsaleable clothes from UnderCover. Her friend only ever gave her things that were too worn or damaged to sell and would have been thrown away otherwise, and Gracie often asked herself who would dream of giving a charity a shirt with all the buttons missing, a duvet cover with rips in it, or curtains that were so faded in places they looked as though the originally plain fabric was striped.

Gracie had recently acquired several large pairs of badly faded curtains from a hotel nearby which was undergoing serious renovations, and she'd been grateful for them. The woman who had bought the hotel had been intending to throw them away because of the condition they were in, but Lottie's husband, Henry, had suggested the lady offer them to Gracie, who had subsequently unpicked them, separating the linings from the body of the curtains, and had cut them up into lengths that were useable.

Gracie picked up a couple of the strips, and some other bits and pieces, then shut up shop for the day. Nearly everyone else had closed already, apart from Sid, so she thought she'd better make tracks and go home.

It wasn't a particularly appealing thought.

She hated to admit it, but she was lonely. Strangely enough, she was lonelier now that she had the shop, than she'd been when she was working out of her tiny front room and hardly saw a soul. Maybe it was due to seeing people all day, and then going home to an empty house – she now had more of an inkling of what she was missing.

Gracie hadn't noticed a banner when she'd passed Vivien's house on her way to work this morning, but she noticed it now all right. As she trotted along the pavement, she couldn't help glancing through the window, hoping for a glimpse of this long-lost son.

However, she was disappointed. All she could see was a shadowy figure as she tried to peep out of the corner of her eye and not make it obvious that she was gawping, and she wasn't even sure whether the figure had been male or not. It could quite as easily have been Vivien as her son.

Gracie dumped her bulging bag on the kitchen worktop as soon as she arrived home and went upstairs to change into her PJs. It might only be six p.m. and still light outside, but she didn't care: comfort was paramount.

After making herself a cup of tea, she took it through to the living room, switched the TV on, and settled down to do some sewing – something she'd vowed not to do when she'd first opened the shop.

The theory had been to separate her working life from her personal life as much as she could. After working in her front room for so long, unable to detect any demarcation between the two, she had initially felt relieved to walk away from her business at the end of the day.

In practice, the relief had lasted less than a week. Gracie had returned to her house and had sat there for four evenings in a row, twiddling her thumbs. She had not made any attempt to teach herself to cook, as she'd vowed. She had not sorted out the weed-filled flowerbeds in the narrow garden. She'd not read the copy of *Crime and Punishment* she'd owned since she was eighteen (she hadn't even peeped inside the cover). And she had not picked up the paintbrush she'd bought to begin some badly needed redecorating.

Instead, her fingers had itched so much to hold a needle that, on day five, she'd given in and had taken up her sewing once more.

The problem was, Gracie didn't regard sewing as work. It was in her blood; it was who she was. And, she was forced to admit, she wasn't happy unless she had a needle and thread in her hand.

Gracie had sewn for as long as she could remember. Her granny had taught her, delighted that one of her three grand-children had shown an interest, and they'd bonded over skeins of embroidery thread and discussions about the various feet available for the old sewing machine Granny had owned.

The best Christmas present Gracie had ever received was a machine of her very own for her twelfth birthday, and she still used it to this day.

However, Gracie did try to stick to some kind of rule to make her feel better about carrying on sewing once she'd closed the shop, and the rule was that she didn't do any paid work at home. The sewing she did at the end of the day whilst curled up in her armchair with the TV on for company was for Catrin and UnderCover, as a thank you (and because it was the right and proper thing to do). Gracie made rag dolls to be sold in the charity shop. Each one was unique and depended solely on whatever scraps of material she had available; and with the majority of those scraps coming from UnderCover itself in the form of clothes and other fabrics which would otherwise be destined for landfill, Gracie thought it was the least she could do.

The arrangement benefited both her and the charity – she got material for free, and in return UnderCover had some lovely dolls to sell.

In fact, Gracie didn't know how she'd manage without Catrin. If she had to buy all the fabric and other bits and pieces she needed, the cost would eat into the small profit she made and her business would quickly become unviable. It was a precarious position to be in, and she hoped for her sake as well as Catrin's that Lucas Grainger was here solely to visit his mum, and not for any other reason.

Chapter 5

Lucas

'Had a nice walk?' his mum asked when Lucas strolled into the kitchen. His sister was sitting at the table, Ruby in her lap.

'Yeah, thanks.'

'I bet Applewell hasn't changed much,' Vivien continued.

'Not really. There are a few new shops.' He briefly considered asking about A Stitch in Time and the woman sitting near the window, but he didn't.

'Are you hungry? There's plenty of food left.' She indicated the cling-film-wrapped plates.

'No, thank you.' He patted his stomach as though he'd eaten his fill, when in reality all he'd done was nibble on a sandwich and half a sausage roll earlier.

'It's there, if you want it – or I could make you something hot?'

'Mum, leave him be.' Nora narrowed her eyes. 'Stop fussing. If Lucas is hungry, he can sort himself out.'

'I know he can, but it's nice to have him home.'

'Whatever. Ianto will be back soon, so I'd better be off.'

Lucas had yet to meet Nora's partner. Nora slid Ruby to the floor. 'Unless you fancy cooking something for *him* as well?' she added sourly.

Vivien looked confused. 'I can if you want—'

'Don't bother.' Nora took Ruby's hand. 'Give Nanna a kiss,' she instructed, and the child took her thumb out of her mouth for long enough to plant a sloppy kiss on her grandmother's cheek.

Nora gave Vivien a one-armed hug as she squashed her mother to her. 'I'll see you tomorrow, OK?'

Vivien nodded. 'I'm at work until four.' She shot Lucas an anxious glance.

'He's a big boy – I'm sure he can amuse himself for a few hours,' Nora said.

'Yes, but…' Vivien chewed her lip.

'Still working at the bakers?' he asked.

'If you came home more often, you'd know where Mum worked,' Nora snapped.

'I phone every week,' Lucas replied, stung. He didn't have to come home every five minutes for their mother to tell him her news.

'I'm still there,' Vivien said. 'Nora, leave it. Please.' She opened the fridge door and stacked two plates inside. Although she had her back to him, he could tell she was upset because the tips of her ears had gone pink. It was funny how he remembered that.

Nora shook her head but didn't say anything further, although Lucas guessed she wanted to. He also guessed she'd say her piece sooner or later.

Nora had every right to be annoyed with him. Although annoyed might be too mild a word for the way she was undoubtedly feeling.

He waited until his sister had left before he began speaking. This might not be the right time, but Lucas wasn't sure if there ever would be a right time, so he might as well get it over with now. He owed his mother that much, and more.

'It wasn't your fault, Mum,' he said. 'It was mine. All mine.'

She stopped what she was doing and turned to look at him, her gaze level. 'It took me a long time to realise that.'

Vivien dropped into the chair his sister had vacated, and suddenly he realised how worn she looked. She was only sixty-two, yet she looked older and frailer than the last time he'd seen her.

'I wracked my brains over and over again, trying to think what I'd done to drive you away.' There were tears in her eyes and they welled up and spilled over to trickle down her cheeks. Each one stabbed him in the chest. 'I couldn't think of a single thing. Why did you run away?'

'Because I was young and thought I knew best.' He drew in a deep breath. 'And because I knew I was going to fail my A-Levels. I hated the thought of letting you down. Of letting my teachers down. And I wanted out of Applewell so bad. I thought I'd get a job and find somewhere to live, because it was London, wasn't it, and the roads were paved with gold.' He shook his head at his naivety. 'Then I'd come back and show you how well I'd done for myself. Ha!'

'At least you phoned to let us know you were OK. Some parents never know.' Her voice shook.

It was true, he *had* phoned her, but only because Effron had made him. He'd been so convinced he'd be able to walk into a job and find somewhere to live – he'd not realised that the contents of his piggybank had been barely enough for a night in a run-down hotel and had been nowhere near what he'd need to rent a room in a shared house for even a week. As for getting a job… you needed an address for that. Third arch on the left wasn't going to cut it.

But by then his stubborn teenage pride had kicked in and he had been unable to face the shame and ignominy of slinking back to Applewell with his tail between his legs.

He'd been so stupid!

His saving grace had been an elderly guy who'd lived on the streets for over forty years, and Lucas's heart constricted when he thought of his friend. *This is for you*, he thought. Lucas had made a promise to Effron that he'd face his past and make peace with it, and he was keeping that promise.

'I almost didn't phone,' he admitted to his mother. Effron had stood over him as he'd dialled the number, guessing that Lucas might chicken out. He'd also held Lucas when he cried after hearing his mother's voice, and he'd done his upmost to persuade Lucas to return home.

It was a pity Lucas hadn't listened to him, because the longer he'd left it the harder it would become, until he told himself his mother and sister were better off without him disrupting their lives.

What an idiot he'd been.

Vivien looked at the ceiling and blinked hard. 'If you hadn't phoned, I don't know what I'd have done. Not knowing was the worst thing in the world. Those first few days after you left...' A sob broke free and she gulped it back.

He knew he'd hurt her; he knew he'd caused her a lot of pain, but at the time he'd been so consumed with his own feelings he hadn't stopped to seriously consider hers. Or Nora's.

'I'm sorry. So, so sorry.'

He should have had this conversation with her the first time he came back to Applewell nearly ten years ago, but it had been such a fleeting visit and his head had been all over the place. He wasn't making excuses: that had been the truth. The simple act of returning after seven long years away had taken all his courage – he hadn't been able to deal with a discussion like this. And each and every subsequent visit had been as fleeting as the first.

He wasn't sure he could deal with it *now*, to be honest, but he knew he had to. For both their sakes. It was time he faced up to what he'd done and try to make amends as best he could.

'Why did you run away?' She repeated and her question was loaded with so much pain, it pierced him to the core.

'Because I wanted more.' He didn't think she'd ever under-stand. How could she, when he didn't understand himself?

'Did you get it?' she asked.

Oh, boy, didn't he just. He'd got so much more than he'd bargained for, and not much of it pleasant. Not for the first few years at least.

He shrugged. 'Maybe.' If he hadn't done what he'd done, then he wouldn't have been in a position to help so many other homeless people. Silver linings...

His mother lifted her chin. 'You're back now, that's all that matters.'

'Not for good,' he warned again. His life was in London – his job, his flat.

She was silent for a while, then she said, 'You haven't spent a night in this house since you left.' And he suddenly understood that him staying with her for however long it might be, meant the world to her.

'I'm sorry,' he repeated, knowing that no matter how often he said it, or how fervently he meant it, it would never be enough to make up for the pain he'd caused her.

'So am I. But what's done is done, and we can't change the past. All any of us can do is look to the future.' She smiled and it was as though the sun had come out. Once again, she was the mum he held in his mind, not the woman he'd seen a few minutes ago.

'Your sister is getting married,' she said.

His own smile was hesitant. 'I know, you told me on the phone.' Despite what Nora thought, he and his mum spoke frequently. Not about what he should have spoken to her about, but at least they'd been in regular contact.

'She's wearing Grandma's dress,' Vivien said.

'Really?'

'I found it in her wardrobe when I cleared her house after she died.'

That was another thing he'd missed – the end of his grandmother's life. He'd made it back to Applewell for the funeral, but he hadn't stayed around long enough to help his mother through her grief.

Sometimes – most of the time – Lucas didn't like himself very much at all.

'I don't know much about weddings and dresses, but wouldn't it be rather old-fashioned?' he said, trying to steer the conversation into less-fraught waters.

'Don't let your sister hear you say that! You'll have to see it, it's beautiful.' His mother's smile was softer now. 'It was originally your great-grandmother's dress. Your grandma wore it for her wedding, and now Nora is wearing it for hers. It's in remarkably good condition, but then it's only been worn on two occasions and has been in a box in the bottom of a wardrobe for the rest of the time. It does smell rather unpleasantly of mothballs, though.' She leant forward and lowered her voice. 'Your great-grandma had a tinier waist than your sister, so Nora is trying to slim into it.'

'What happens if she doesn't?'

'Shh! Don't go there. And whatever you do, don't eat a burger in front of her or she'll flip her lid.'

'I thought she was vegetarian?'

'That was when she was fourteen.'

Fourteen was the age Nora had been when he'd left. There were three years between them. His sister used to look up to him once – he didn't think she did now.

'What's Ianto like?' Lucas asked.

Vivien rested her chin on the back of her hand. 'He's a decent man. He loves her and Ruby to bits, and I believe he'll take care of her.'

'Nora doesn't need taking care of,' he joked, remembering how headstrong and determined she was.

His mother gave him a level look. 'She does.'

'But she—' He stopped.

Vivien rose to her feet and resumed stacking the uneaten food in the fridge. 'She's not the same as she was seventeen years ago. None of us are. People change.'

His mother was right – people did change. He had, and he hoped it was for the better. The next few weeks in Applewell and in his mother's house would tell.

'Leave it out?' he asked, nodding at the plate of assorted sandwiches she was about to put away.

She took the cling film off and popped it on the table. 'Sausage roll?'

'Go on, then.' He wasn't hungry per se, but he could prob-ably manage something, and she'd gone to all that trouble. 'Shall

I make us a cup of tea?' He preferred coffee these days, but he knew she still drank copious amounts of tea.

'I'll do it,' she said. She flicked the switch on the kettle, her back to him. 'How do you take it, these days?'

'Um…' How *did* he take his tea? It was so long since he'd drunk any. 'As it comes, milk, no sugar, please. But you needn't wait on me, Mum.'

'I want to.' She waved a hand in the air. 'You'll be gone soon enough, so…'

He understood, but he'd been independent for so long that it was going to be hard to let her fuss over him. And Nora had made it clear she wasn't happy about it. He'd have to try to make sure she didn't have her nose put out of joint too much; she'd been their mother's sole focus for so many years that she was bound to find his return difficult. But at least there was Ruby to distract her and the wedding to concentrate on.

As he ate, his mother tidying up around him whilst taking slurps of her tea, he thought about Ruby. Maybe he'd buy her one of those cute dolls in UnderCover…

When he'd last seen her she'd been a toddler, all chubby thighs and nappy-padded bottom. Now though, she was starting to get leggy, taller and slimmer, more like a child than a baby. She looked like Nora, the same curling hair, the same dark almond-shaped eyes. Although Lucas and his sister had similar hair colour, their eyes were different. His were blue, a throwback to his grandfather on his mother's side, while Nora followed their father.

Not for the first time Lucas wondered if he'd have left Applewell had his dad been around. He suspected he probably would have, but not the way he'd done it and certainly not at seventeen. He'd have resat his A-Levels (or perhaps he would have done better the first time around) and would have gone to university. He wouldn't have run away, but he would have left Applewell eventually. The world was a big place and he'd always wanted to see more of it.

What he'd seen instead was the nastier, dirtier side of London. Not what he'd hoped for.

Apparently, his father had felt the same way about Applewell, but he'd gone even further afield to Alaska.

At least Lucas hadn't gone that far.

It seemed that running away was a family trait – although that wasn't an excuse for what Lucas had done or the pain he'd caused.

His mother had never married again, and if she'd had any love interests between then and now he'd never got to hear about it. Maybe that wasn't the kind of thing his mum wanted to announce over the phone? If he and Nora could have a conversation without her biting his head off, he'd ask her. There was so much he didn't know, so much he'd missed out on. So much catching up to do.

The rest of the evening was spent amicably enough, he and his mum watching TV, him getting a take-away later because neither of them had eaten a proper meal. The leftovers in the fridge no longer appealed, and he didn't want his mum to start cooking at nine o'clock when she had work in the morning. She refused to let him anywhere near the kitchen, so he'd nipped out and bought battered fish and hot fluffy chips which they'd eaten with their fingers out of the paper.

Suddenly, with the smell of vinegar in his nose and the lingering taste of salt on his lips, Lucas was transported back to his childhood, and for the first time in many, many years he felt he belonged somewhere.

It was a strange and unnerving feeling, but not an unwelcome one.

Chapter 6

Gracie

The Busy Bumble always lived up to its name on Friday nights. The food was inexpensive and plentiful, there was a decent variety of dishes on the menu, the music wasn't too loud that you couldn't hear yourself think (*I must be getting old*, Gracie thought) and the drinks weren't extortionate. Combine all those elements with a mix of locals and tourists, and it made for a pleasant and lively evening out.

Gracie was the first to arrive and she nabbed a free table, then waved at a member of the bar staff to order some drinks. 'Catrin,' she mouthed pointing to the empty chair next to her, and the barmaid nodded. It was a distinct advantage when you regularly ordered the same drink, so when Catrin arrived a glass of white wine was waiting for her and Gracie was happily sipping a half pint of lager.

'Busy, isn't it?' Gracie observed, scanning the room, nodding and smiling shyly to those she recognised.

'Yeah, well, it's building up to the school holidays, so it's to be expected,' Catrin said. Applewell was always bustling in the summer months.

'Any news?' Gracie asked, as they didn't have the chance to have a proper chat yesterday.

Catrin took a huge gulp of wine. 'I met him – Lucas Grainger.'

'You did? What's he like?'

'Seriously good-looking.'

'Behave. You're married, or as good as.'

'I can look, can't I?' Catrin sighed and stared at the table. 'I still don't know why he's in Applewell, though.' She paused. 'Actually, now I come to think of it, you saw him yourself.'

'When?' Gracie thought hard. She'd barely noticed anyone yesterday or today. She'd been too busy shortening a fuchsia pink dress with the most wonderful beading on the bodice, and nipping it in at the waist. The girl who would be wearing it to her prom was petite.

'Yesterday, when you came into UnderCover. Remember I went out the back to fetch that bag of stuff for you, and you shouted to say I had a customer? That was him.'

'It never was!'

'Uh-huh.' Catrin nodded.

Gracie remembered him very well indeed, especially since she'd spotted him later, standing outside Sid's newsagents. He'd been looking at the notices in the window, but he'd glanced her way and their eyes had met. She could still feel the tingle that the brief look had sent through her.

'I thought he was a tourist,' Gracie said.

'I wish he had been,' Catrin muttered. 'Oh, shoot! Don't look now, but here he is.'

'He's in The Busy Bumble?' Gracie twisted around in her seat.

'I said, *don't look*,' Catrin hissed.

Hastily, Gracie turned back again, but not before she'd caught a glimpse of a tall, broad-shouldered man standing near the bar.

Catrin attacked her wine. 'What's he doing here?' she demanded, peering at him over the rim of her glass.

'Having a drink?' Gracie hazarded a guess.

'I meant in Applewell, not in The Busy Bumble. Duh.'

'No need to get tetchy.'

'You'd be tetchy if your job was on the line,' Catrin retorted.

Gracie didn't like to say it, but her business *might* be on the line if Catrin's fears were realised. Although Gracie had always done alterations, the money it brought in wasn't enough to live on. Making things out of scraps of material was her bread and butter, and A Stitch in Time was the perfect showcase for that.

When she'd been working out of her front room, she'd relied almost exclusively on selling online, plus the odd few sales which came in from those local shops that had been kind enough to stock some of her wares. Even now, with a shop of her own, she still continued to sell online, but was relying on it less and less as time went on.

'He didn't give any hint?' Gracie asked. She was dying to have another look at him, but she kept her curiosity in check.

'He mentioned something about streamlining and maximising profits, but what he intends to do to make that happen is anyone's guess.' Catrin's glass was empty. 'I'll get us another.' She made to get out of her seat, but swiftly sat down again. 'I'll give it a minute,' she said, then, 'Oh, no, he's coming over.'

Gracie became aware of someone standing directly behind her, and she thought she could smell a woody, citrus scent.

'Catrin, nice to see you again,' a deep male voice said. 'Can I buy you both a drink?'

Gracie turned to look at him and was confronted by the waistband of his jeans. Her eyes travelled up and up, until they eventually reached his face. Gosh, he was tall.

'Hello, again.' He smiled down at her.

'Hello,' she squeaked. She cleared her throat and tried again, this time in a more normal tone of voice. 'Hi.'

'Are you a volunteer?' he asked.

'For what?'

'UnderCover.' He looked from her to Catrin.

'This is my friend, Gracie Stewart. She owns A Stitch in Time on the high street,' Catrin said.

'I see.' A small line dissected his brow and Gracie wondered what it was he saw in her to make him frown.

Catrin said, 'Gracie, this is Lucas Grainger. He works for UnderCover, but I'm not really sure what it is he does.'

'Sorry, I should have explained.' Lucas smiled down at them. 'Let me get you a drink, then I'll tell you. What are you having?'

'White wine, please.' Catrin handed him her glass.

Gracie hadn't finished her drink yet, and she wasn't going to be rushed. 'I'm fine, thanks.'

'If you're sure…?'

'I am.' Gracie held her glass tightly as though she expected him to wrestle it from her. Feeling silly, she put it on the table.

'She'll have half a lager, please,' Catrin said, adding, 'What?' as soon as Lucas had walked away. 'Why are you looking at me like that?'

'You're potentially accepting drinks from the enemy,' Gracie said.

'Hey, a free drink is a free drink, and I've never known you to turn one down before.'

'I have, actually,' Gracie said. Although not often, she thought. She only said no if it was offered by a tourist, because they were trying to chat her up and she couldn't be dealing with all that. If the drink was being offered by someone she knew, that was an altogether different thing.

'What do you think?' Catrin asked out of the corner of her mouth.

'He's very good-looking.'

Catrin squinted at her. 'I meant, the reason he's in Applewell?'

'Oh, right. I've no idea. He said he'd explain.'

'Shh, stop talking – he's coming back.'

'You started it—' Gracie broke off abruptly as half a lager appeared on the table in front of her. 'Thanks.'

'You're welcome.' Lucas pulled out a chair. 'May I?' he asked.

'Please do. We're dying to hear more about you.' Catrin was wearing her brightest smile.

He sat and Gracie waited for him to swallow a mouthful of beer, her gaze never leaving his face.

He set his glass down and smiled at her.

Gracie felt a blush creeping up her neck and she hurriedly looked away.

'You were going to tell us what you do at UnderCover,' Catrin reminded him.

'I'm the Philanthropy Manager.'

'The what now?'

'Philanthropy. My job is to acquire major gifts from donors.'

'Come again?' Catrin was looking at him as though he'd suddenly grown two heads.

He sighed. 'I get this all the time. I persuade people and corporations to donate large sums of money to the charity.'

'Based in UnderCover's head office?' Catrin asked.

'Yes.'

'In London?'

'Yes.'

'So what are you doing here? *Oh!*' She clapped one hand to her mouth and flapped the other in the air. 'Who is it? Who's buying a place in Applewell? Is it Luke Evans? You know – he was in *The Hobbit* and *The Girl on the Train*. He's Welsh.'

'I'm sorry...?' The crease between Lucas's brows was back, Gracie noticed.

'Who you are here to schmooze.' Catrin explained.

'I'm not here to schmooze anyone.'

'But that's what you do, right? You persuade people to give money to the charity?'

'That's right. Amongst other things.'

'So who are you in Applewell to persuade?'

'No one.'

'I don't follow.'

Gracie could see that Catrin was genuinely confused. She wished she could help, but she was just as perplexed as her friend.

'I'm not here to persuade anyone to do anything,' Lucas insisted.

'Then why *are* you here?' Catrin had a worried look on her face again. His arrival had really unsettled her, Gracie thought.

'As I said, to see if we can streamline anything and maximise profits.'

'Yeah, you said.' Catrin downed the rest of her wine.

Wordlessly Gracie pushed her untouched lager towards her and Catrin gave her a tiny, grateful smile.

Lucas got to his feet. 'It was nice seeing you again,' he said to Catrin. 'No doubt I'll see you soon. And you too, Gracie.' He seemed to hesitate, and Gracie wondered if he was going to say anything else.

He didn't, and she watched him return to the bar where he propped himself up on one elbow. Very soon Donald Mousel, who was technically retired but drove a taxi to supplement his pension, engaged him in conversation.

'I'm none the wiser,' Catrin said. 'Are you?'

'Not in the slightest.'

'I still think he's up to something.' Catrin's eyes were narrowed and she was glaring at him over the rim of her glass.

'This isn't like you,' Gracie said. 'Are you really so worried about losing your job?'

Without warning, Catrin's eyes filled with tears. She looked up at the ceiling, her face reddening as she blinked rapidly, and she fanned herself with her hands. 'Sorry,' she gulped. 'I don't know what's got into me.'

'This isn't just about Lucas Grainger and UnderCover, is it?'

Catrin's face crumpled. 'No.' Her voice was small, and Gracie had to strain to hear it above the noise in the pub. 'It's Gareth. He says he wants us to take a break.'

'But you guys have been together forever!' Gracie was shocked. She'd always considered them the perfect couple – if they were splitting up what hope was there for anyone else?

'That's the problem, he says. He wants to "spread his wings".' She mimicked air-quotes around the phrase.

'When did he tell you this?'

'Wednesday evening, after I got home from work.'

'You've been sitting on this for two whole days and you didn't think to tell me?'

'There wasn't anything you could have done,' Catrin said miserably.

'I could have given you a shoulder to cry on. I still can. You know you can tell me anything, right? I'll always be here for you.'

'I know, and I'm going to take you up on the offer of a shoulder. But to be honest, I was hoping it would simply blow over.'

'Has he moved out?'

Catrin shook her head. 'Not yet, but he says he's going to if he can get one of his mates to put him up.'

'Oh, my lovely, I'm so sorry. What do you think he meant by spreading his wings? Does he want to travel, see new places?'

Her friend snorted. 'So he says. He says we got together too young.'

Gracie was stunned. This was the last thing she expected to hear. 'Is there… you know…?'

'Anyone else? Not as far as I know, but I suppose it's only a matter of time. All I hope is that he's moved out by then, otherwise I don't think I'll be able to bear it. I don't know how I'll cope as it is.' Catrin turned her stricken face to Gracie.

Never had Gracie felt so useless. 'If there's anything I can do, anything at all…'

Catrin tipped the rest of the lager into her mouth and swallowed. 'It is what it is. I'm just going to have to deal with it. Fancy another?'

'Why not?' Gracie finished her own drink and gave Catrin the empty glass, her gaze following her friend as she made her way to the bar.

Lucas was still there, having his ear chewed off by the garrulous Donald, and a couple of others had joined him.

Gracie gave George Nightingale a wave, and he waved back. Gracie had a lot of time for George – he was a man after her own heart in that he didn't like to waste things. It was 'his waste not, want not' attitude that had led to him becoming a hoarder, but she was the same in that she hated throwing anything away, whether it be an inch of fabric, a broken zip, or an odd button.

Her gaze came to rest on Lucas once more, and she realised he was staring at her. He glanced away before she did, but not before she'd seen something in his eyes that gave her pause.

Then Gracie shook her head at her silliness. For a second there she'd thought he was interested in her. But he couldn't have been.

Gracie wasn't the interesting type.

Chapter 7

Lucas

When Lucas woke the next morning, it took him a few moments to orientate himself. His immediate thought was to wonder where the hell he was, followed by a groan when he realised he'd come full circle and was lying in his boyhood bed.

Unnerved by the absence of background noise that was a constant in London, this was the second night in a row that it had taken him ages to drop off to sleep and he'd jerked awake several times, unused to the silence. He'd finally fallen into a deep slumber at around four a.m. and was now feeling heavy-lidded and sluggish. When he checked the time he saw why – it was gone ten.

Cross, he hastily stumbled out of bed, despite having nowhere to go and nothing to do. There was no need for him to rise at his normal six thirty, but he felt as though he should, and he was now somewhat out of sorts. He'd been in Applewell less than two days and it was already making its mark.

The house was silent, and he strained to hear signs that his mother was downstairs, before realising she must be at work.

That's where he should rightly be, and guilt swamped him.

He stood under the shower to try to wash it away, telling himself that everyone needed a break, that it was normal to take a holiday. That's all this visit to Applewell was – an extended holiday.

Once dressed, he went downstairs and into the kitchen in search of breakfast. Yesterday morning when he'd done the same thing, he'd been oddly touched and slightly appalled to discover that his mother had stocked the cupboard with Coco Pops and Nutella. They'd been his favourite foods once. His tastes had matured since then, but he'd poured himself a bowl of cereal anyway and had made some white-bread toast and spread it liberally with the nutty paste, and had instantly been transported back in time.

This morning he couldn't face it. He needed something more grownup, something that reflected who he was now, not who he'd been back then. It was sweet and thoughtful of her, but…

After moping around for most of yesterday, setting up his laptop and trying to do some work (how could he not, when UnderCover had been his life for so long?), he'd taken the bull by the horns and had descended on the pub last night. He had the feeling his mother had been relieved to see him go out, but that hadn't been his sole reason for having a pint in The Busy Bumble. He knew the residents of Applewell would be agog for news about him, so he thought he might as well get it over with. They'd soon get used to seeing him around, but if he hid away he'd be a sensation any time he stepped outside his front door.

Not *his* front door, his mum's. His own front door was nearly two hundred and fifty miles away.

Deciding to go in search of breakfast and shop for the foods he liked, Lucas grabbed his keys and set off.

He managed three steps before he was stopped by his mum's next-door neighbour.

'Off out, then?' Mrs Hayworth asked. 'Going anywhere nice?' She looked pointedly at his car.

He put his keys in his pocket to indicate he was walking. 'Just to the shops.'

'It's a nice day for it.'

'It certainly is.' Though he wasn't sure what, exactly, it was a nice day for. Did the weather have to be nice to make buying some fruit and yoghurt a pleasant experience?

44

'I expect your mum is glad to have you back,' she said.

Mrs Hayworth lived right next door. She had seen the banner. She'd been on the pavement when he'd arrived, and she'd eaten a sausage roll or two from the table in his mother's living room. She already knew his mother was pleased, so she was fishing for information. Mrs Hayworth wanted to know why he was in Applewell.

'I expect,' was all he said. If *he* wasn't totally sure why he was back, how could he enlighten anyone else?

'Well, I best let you get on,' she said. 'You've probably got things to do.'

'Nice talking to you,' he replied, giving her a wave as he strode down the pavement and trying to ignore how claustrophobic her nosiness made him feel.

He gave UnderCover a surreptitious glance as he walked past, checking its level of busyness and was glad to see there were several customers in the shop. He also noticed that the window display had changed since his visit on Thursday. Either some of the items had been sold, or Catrin liked to ring the changes.

Applewell had a mix of locals and tourists at this time of year, so the main street was a hive of activity. It was a thriving little village with an eclectic mix of artisan shops, such as the bakers where his mum worked, and ones which would appeal more to tourists, and he grinned at the colourful display of inflatables, buckets, spades and fishing nets outside one of them. It brought back memories of long days spent at the beach, rock-pooling and making enormous constructions out of sand.

Lucas wondered if the cove he used to go to was just as undiscovered and unspoilt as it had been in his youth. He hoped so, and on impulse he nipped into the shop selling beachy stuff and picked out an elaborate bucket with four turrets in a garish shade of pink and a spade in the same colour, and hoped Ruby would love them.

After buying them, though, he had second thoughts. His niece didn't know him from Adam and here he was buying her a bucket and spade, and hoping he'd be able to take her to the beach. He halted outside the shop, wondering what the hell he'd been thinking and debating whether to take them back for a refund.

He dithered for a while, then shrugged; he'd bought them now, so he might as well hang on to them. He'd give them to Ruby anyway, if Nora would let him. Knowing his sister, she'd probably accuse him of trying to buy his niece's affections.

Feeling ridiculous, he darted into Eleri Jones's cafe and took a seat at the nearest free table.

'Look what the cat's dragged in,' a female voice said, and Lucas glanced around to see Eleri Jones standing at his elbow. 'You haven't changed a bit,' she announced.

'Neither have you.' He'd have recognised Eleri anywhere.

'Still got that moody look on your face,' she said.

Had he? Lucas hadn't realised. 'I can't help the way my face hangs,' he said, a little defensively.

'I like the bucket and spade. The colour suits you.'

'Very funny. It's for my niece, Ruby. Nora's little girl.'

'I know who Ruby is.' Her tone suggested that she knew Ruby far better than he did. 'What brings you back to Applewell?' Trust Eleri not to beat about the bush. She'd always been forthright.

'Work, holiday…' He trailed off, unsure what to call it.

'Which is it?'

'Both?'

'Are you asking me, or telling me?'

'Telling you.' Goodness, she definitely hadn't changed. 'Is this your place?'

'My name's above the door, so, duh, I suppose it must be. Are you ready to order?'

'Um, yeah. Do you have granary bread?'

Eleri gazed at him, her expression unreadable. 'I have whole-wheat, sourdough, rye, multigrain, ciabatta, and today I also have focaccia. How would you like it – as part of a sandwich, on its own, toasted, with scrambled egg…?'

'Do you do much trade?' If she was as sarcastic as this to all her customers…

'Look around. What do you see?' Eleri put her hands on her hips and glared at him. The cafe was almost full.

'I was being… Never mind.'

'I know what you were being. Can I take your order, or what?'

'Multigrain toast, please, with bacon and eggs.' Stuff being healthy, the smell of bacon was making his mouth water.

'Beans, mushrooms, grilled tomatoes?'

'Just the bacon, eggs and toast, please.'

'Coffee, tea, asses' milk?'

'I don't suppose I could have a dirty chai latte?'

'You suppose right, but I could stick a teabag in a latte if that floats your boat?'

His lips twitched.

Eleri broke into a grin. 'You're a prat, Lucas Grainger, did you know that?'

'I've been called worse. Flat white, please.'

'Coming right up.' She turned to leave. 'Good to have you back, Lucas.'

He nearly said it was good to *be* back, but he didn't. He nodded instead, earning himself another one of her looks, and it made him squirm.

He sat quietly for a while, eating his breakfast and staring out of the window. It wasn't until Eleri came to clear away his plate and bring him a second coffee that she said anything further.

'There's a rumour going around about you,' she said, picking up his used napkin and putting it on the plate.

'Just the one?'

Her look told him there were probably plenty. 'The one I'm interested in is that you're here to do Catrin out of a job.'

'*Really?* I can assure you I'm not.' Lucas was astonished. How had anyone arrived at such a conclusion? He'd only been in Applewell five minutes.

'The word is that you're either going to manage UnderCover yourself, or you're closing it down.'

'The word is wrong.'

'Why *are* you here, then?'

'Is that any of your business?'

'No, but people want to know.'

'By people, you mean *you*?'

'I admit I'm nosey.'

'Yeah, you and most of Applewell.'

'There's bound to be conjecture,' she said. 'If you're not going to sack Catrin, you need to tell her. She's worried sick.'

'If people minded their own business and didn't gossip, then there wouldn't be a rumour in the first place.'

'This is Applewell you're talking about. We look out for each other.'

'I'll speak to Catrin after I've finished my coffee.'

'Make sure you do,' was Eleri's parting shot as he paid and left.

Feeling slightly shell-shocked, Lucas walked into Under-Cover, his head reeling from his encounter with Eleri. He wasn't sure what to make of it, to be honest. Had he come across as a pretentious git who thought anywhere other than London was out in the sticks? Or had she been winding him up? Perhaps it had been a bit of both, because he had to admit he *had* been surprised at the range of bread on offer. The rest of the items on the menu had been equally as impressive. Take the daily special, for instance: stuffed peppers. It was a far cry from the sausage and chips he remembered the cafe serving when he was a kid. It had been a proper greasy spoon back then.

Lucas lingered near the bookshelf for a while, not wanting to intrude whilst Catrin was serving, and he waited until she was free before making his presence known.

'Can I have a quick word?' he asked her. There was a volunteer in the shop so maybe they could chat in private away from the shop floor. 'Through here?' He opened the door to the stock room and the kitchen area beyond and ushered her through it. 'This won't take long.'

He halted as soon as Catrin shut the door behind her, and he noted the dark circles under her eyes that hadn't been in evidence the last time he'd spoken to her.

'I owe you an apology,' he said. 'I've heard a rumour that I'm here to take over from you or close the place down, but I can assure you that isn't the case. I'm here to... see my family, and to... have a break.' He was trying to explain, without going into detail. 'It's a holiday, of sorts, but while I'm here I thought I'd try to see what can be done to maximise profits.'

'So you said.' She didn't sound convinced.

'I'm not here for any other reason; your job is perfectly safe.'

He thought she'd be pleased and relieved.

He certainly didn't expect her to burst into tears. Awkwardly, he shuffled from foot to foot, wondering if he should give her a hug, leave, or make her a cup of tea. In the end he settled for giving her arm a rub and popping into the staff toilet for some loo roll and handing her a length.

'Sorry,' she snuffled, her nose in the tissue.

'I didn't realise you were so worried about my presence in Applewell,' he said, perching on the edge of the battered ancient desk and feeling at a loss.

'It's not that,' she said. 'Well, it is part of it.' She blew her nose. 'It's mostly Gareth, my partner. He wants a break. From me. Us.'

'Oh, right. I'm sorry.'

'Me, too.'

'Do you need some time off to sort this out?' he asked, but when she shot him a suspicious look, he held up his hands and said, 'No ulterior motive – honest.'

She dabbed at her eyes. 'I'll be better off working, keeping busy,' she said. 'Too much time to think otherwise.'

'Fair enough, but the offer is there if you need it.'

'Thanks.' She blew her nose again, her sniffles under control. 'I'm sorry you had to see that.'

'I've seen worse.'

'I must look a sight.'

'You look a little upset,' he said, 'but other than that you look fine.' He straightened up. 'While I'm here, is there anything I can do? Shop-wise, I mean. I'm at a loose end, so if you can use me, use me.' It was many years since he'd done a stint in an UnderCover shop, but he quite fancied the idea.

There was that look again – suspicion and mistrust.

'No strings, no ulterior motive,' he assured her. 'It'll give me something to do, and I might get an idea or two.'

'To maximise profits?'

He smiled. 'Exactly.'

'This is a charity, not a business,' she pointed out, throwing the crumpled piece of loo roll in the bin.

'True, but after the wages, the rents, the council tax, the utility bills, the transport costs and so on are paid, anything left over is deemed to be profit. Actually, it's called a surplus, and the money is ploughed straight back into where it's needed most – shelters, kitchens, fundraising.'

'Paying your salary?' she asked, archly.

'That, too. However, if I do my job right, I can pull in more money from just one benefactor than a shop makes in six months.'

'If that's the case, you might as well close the shop down,' she said glumly.

'Every bit helps, and we all play a part. This shop – all of our shops – are equally valuable to the charity. They are UnderCover's bread and butter. All I do is spread a little jam on it now and again.'

And how heartily sick of it he was. Not sick of raising funds; he was sick of trying to persuade people who had more money than they could possibly spend in a lifetime, to part with what was (to them) a tiny percentage of it. He was sick and tired of seeing how the rich lived, knowing there were people on the streets with only the contents of a couple of plastic bags to their names. The disparity had been chipping away at him bit by bit, and now he felt physically ill whenever he thought about it.

Effron's sad death had been the final straw, the nail in the coffin of Lucas's emotional and mental wellbeing. Despite Lucas's pleading and begging, Effron had refused Lucas's offer of a roof over his head. As soon as Lucas was off the streets and had a place of his own, he'd beseeched Effron to move in with him, but he hadn't been able to persuade him. Effron had claimed he was too old and too set in his ways, and he'd compared himself to a feral cat who would hate to be caged in a house. He'd stayed over now and again, relishing the feel of clean skin, clean clothes, and a hot meal, but he'd never slept in the bed in Lucas's spare room – he'd always taken the duvet off and placed it on the floor – and in the morning he'd be gone again.

His stubbornness and determination to live the way he'd wanted had been the death of him. A British winter was no friend to the homeless, despite Lucas making sure the old man had warm, waterproof clothing and as much food as he could eat.

Effron's death had cut Lucas to the quick.

Jonas had noticed he was struggling and had persuaded him to take some time away from work before he burnt out totally. 'Relax, have a holiday,' his boss had said.

The problem was, Lucas didn't know how to relax, and he certainly didn't feel like going on holiday. Neither did he feel like holing up in a cottage in the middle of Scotland, or on the Isle of Man, or somewhere equally remote.

He had done the only thing he could think of, and the one thing Effron had made him promise to do – he'd come home.

But now he was here, he had no idea what he was supposed to do next.

Chapter 8

Gracie

Lucas Grainger seemed to be popping up everywhere, Gracie thought, when she saw him striding down the high street. He had a garishly pink bucket and spade in one hand, and he looked as though he was trying to pretend they were nothing to do with him. In the other he carried one of her squashy dolls, so he'd clearly paid a visit to UnderCover this morning. He slowed as he reached A Stitch in Time, his attention caught by her window display, the centrepiece of which was a large and glorious quilt, and she was able to study him for a moment.

He was just as handsome as she remembered from last night in the pub. More so, with the sun on his face.

Gracie was so focused on him that she jumped a mile when her phone rang, and she let out a squeak.

'Guess what?' Catrin sounded brighter than she'd done last night in the pub.

'You and Gareth have sorted out your differences?' Catrin and Gareth were made for each other, and if he couldn't see that, he was an idiot, Gracie thought, keeping her eyes on the man who was looking at the elaborate quilt.

'No...' Catrin said sadly, and Gracie was immediately contrite.

'Sorry, Cat, I just assumed—'

'Lucas has just left the shop. He came in to tell me he'd heard the rumours and that my job is safe.'

Gracie's eyes tracked him as he walked up to the door of her own shop. The little bell above it tinkled when he pushed it open. 'That's good,' she said, absently.

'You don't sound very pleased.'

'I *am*,' she said hurriedly. 'It's just—'

'He's really nice. God knows what he thought about me, though. When he told me the rumours were false, I burst into tears.'

Gracie refrained from pointing out that it was Catrin herself who'd leapt to conclusions and had assumed he wasn't in Applewell solely to visit his mum. 'Good,' she said, instead.

'It wasn't good – he must think I'm a right idiot. And then I went and told him about Gareth.'

'You did?'

Lucas had his back to her and was looking at a selection of fabric-covered photo frames on the dresser, whilst Gracie studied him. He had a nice backside for a guy: not too scrawny but not too chunky either. His legs were long and encased in black denim, his back straight and broad, and his hair curled slightly where it met the collar of his chambray shirt.

Catrin carried on, 'He was awfully nice about it – he even asked me if I needed to take some time off. I told him no, of course. Despite what he said about my job, I don't want to give him ideas.'

'Like what?'

He was now examining a lampshade she'd made out of tying loads of strips of fabric onto an old wire lampshade frame. It was really pretty and effective, even if she did say so herself.

'Like I can easily be replaced,' Catrin said. 'Oops, I'd better go; some customers have just come in.'

'OK, bye.' Gracie put the phone down, her attention on Lucas. 'Are you looking for anything in particular?' she called over to him.

Lucas turned around. 'Did you make this?' He pointed to the lampshade.

'Yes, I did.'

'A bit risky, isn't it?'

'What do you mean?'

'Using fabric for a lampshade.'

Gracie bristled. 'I think you'll find that many lampshades are made out of fabric.'

He blinked and thought for a moment. 'I suppose they are.'

'And this one is sprayed with fire retardant, as are any others I make. I can assure you it's perfectly safe.'

'Sorry.'

Gracie nodded, acknowledging his apology.

'I seem to be upsetting everyone today,' he continued.

'Oh? Anyone I know?' Gracie asked, innocently.

'Your friend Catrin, Eleri Jones, and now you.'

She wondered what he'd said to Eleri to cheese her off. Catrin, she knew all about. 'She's really nice, you know. Loves her job and is good at it, too.'

'Eleri?'

'Oh, yes, her as well, but I was referring to Catrin.'

'Right.' Lucas fell silent.

'*Are* you looking for anything in particular?' she asked after the silence stretched to an uncomfortable length.

He held up his hands, showing her the bucket and spade, and the doll. 'I seem to have been buying presents for my niece, so I thought I'd better get something for my mum, and maybe my sister.'

'Your mum would love a bunch of flowers,' Gracie suggested.

'Good idea.' He looked slightly startled.

'There's a decent florist further up the road.'

'What about my sister?'

'Nora? Hmm, let me think.' Gracie tapped her chin as she glanced around the shop. 'I wonder...'

'Do you know her well?'

'As well as I know most people in Applewell,' she said.

'So, intimately, then?'

54

Gracie laughed at his dry tone. 'I bet you're finding it different to London.'

'You could say that. Any ideas?'

'Huh?'

'Nora.'

'You could offer to babysit?'

'You're not a very good salesperson, are you?' He smiled at her. 'I would have thought you'd have suggested an item from here.'

'Selling isn't my forte.'

'Yet you own a shop?'

'I admit I prefer sewing to selling, but I have to fund my habit, so I sell what I make or I charge for the sewing I do.'

'You've got a wide variety of things.' He bent to read one of the several notices dotted around the shop, then he looked up at her. 'It says that everything is individual and made from recycled fabric?'

'Not a scrap of fabric is new. Everything was something else in a previous life. All except the thread.'

'I like the ethos, and the name – A Stitch in Time.'

'It's not very original, but it'll do. And it's quite apt, as a stitch in time does save nine. If a seam starts to unravel it's best to repair it immediately and not wait for it to get worse.'

'Most people wouldn't bother repairing it at all.'

'It does depend on what it is. Excuse me.' Gracie heard the bell tinkle and when she saw who her customer was, she walked forward with her hands outstretched in greeting. 'Barbara, how lovely to see you. Have you brought the gown with you?' She gave the woman's hands a squeeze, then released her.

'Here.' Barbara took a tissue-wrapped parcel out of her bag and passed it to her.

Gracie took it reverently and went over to her sewing table.

'Do you think you can do anything with it?' Barbara asked, and Gracie heard the concern in her voice.

'Let's take a look, shall we?' Carefully, she removed the tissue paper, revealing the most exquisite christening gown. It was quite old and must have cost a fortune when new.

After examining it, Gracie glanced up to see Barbara looking at Lucas out of the corner of her eye.

'If you need to serve this gentleman...' Barbara said, hopefully.

'It's OK, he's just looking.'

'He's Vivien's son, isn't he?' Barbara asked, and to Gracie's amusement and Barbara's consternation, the man himself replied.

'That's me, Lucas Grainger.'

'Oh, er, hello.' Barbara's expression was one of excitement with a hint of discomfort. Gracie guessed she would be on the phone to her friends to say she'd met Lucas, the second she was out of the door.

Gracie felt rather sorry for Lucas, and for his mum. It wasn't easy being the centre of attention in Applewell, but she knew it would soon blow over and in a matter of days the gossipmongers would find someone or something else to focus on.

'Hi.' He nodded and smiled at Barbara, then went back to wandering around the shop.

Barbara raised her eyebrows and gave Gracie a meaningful stare.

'Have you got the baby's measurements?' Gracie asked, ignoring the gesture.

'Oh, right, yes.' Barbara rooted around in her purse and brought out a folded sheet of paper. 'You will be careful with it, won't you?' She stroked the gown lovingly. 'I've had all mine christened in it without any bother, but this new baby is bigger than any of mine were at the time of their christening. If Asha had made her mind up sooner to have him christened, then we wouldn't be in this mess.'

Gracie would hardly call the situation a mess, but she knew how much it meant to Barbara to have her first grandchild wear the gown his father had worn when he'd been christened.

Gracie studied the piece of paper, then she measured the gown. It was doable, but she'd have to unpick a seam or two.

'I can make it bigger,' she said, 'but it will mean inserting some panels here, here and here.' She pointed out the seams in question. 'If you bring it back to me after the ceremony, I'll take them out again, and no one will know they'd ever been there.'

'You can do that?' Barbara squinted at her suspiciously.

'You wouldn't have brought it to me if you thought I couldn't,' Gracie pointed out.

'I suppose not.' Barbara looked a little happier. 'And you can have it ready in time?'

'Absolutely.'

'OK, then, if you're sure?'

'I'm sure.' Gracie rewrapped the precious garment in its tissue paper and popped it in a shallow box and put a lid on it. 'It will be perfectly safe with me,' she said, writing Barbara's name on a sticky label and smoothing it onto the lid.

When Barbara felt sufficiently reassured that her gown would be kept safe, she allowed herself to be shown to the door, casting the odd curious glance in Lucas's direction as she went.

With one customer gone, Gracie turned her attention to her other one. 'Is there anything else I can help you with?' she asked Lucas.

'Babysitting?'

'I'm sorry?' Did he need her to help him babysit?

'You suggested I offered to babysit for Nora.'

'Oh, yes, that's right.' Was that so strange?

'Why?'

'Because the perfect gift for a busy mum is time.'

Gracie squirmed under his scrutiny, and she wondered what was going through his mind as he gazed at her. She knew what he was seeing – a face remarkable for its sheer ordinariness, topped with that unruly hair of hers – but she didn't know what he was actually *thinking*. Although she could probably guess it was about something or someone else entirely, and he just happened to be looking in her direction whilst he was thinking it.

People, men especially, didn't often look at Gracie. They usually looked through her or over her, and being overlooked was partly to do with her height (she was only just over five foot) but mostly it had to do with the fact that she was totally unexceptional; apart from her sewing skills, but that was hardly a reason for a member of the opposite sex to give her a second glance. She counted herself lucky if she received a first...

'That's rather insightful and quite altruistic,' Lucas said. 'I thought you would have tried to flog me something, which you could have done very easily considering I know next to nothing about what my mother or my sister might like.'

'What good would that do?'

'Excuse me?'

'You might spend a few pounds in my shop, but neither Vivien nor Nora would get what they'd truly like.'

'Flowers?'

'I doubt your mother has many bunches bought for her.' She saw a flash of guilt in his eyes, which faded as quickly as it appeared. 'She likes peonies,' Gracie added.

'Not roses?'

She shook her head.

'And babysitting for Nora?'

'Vivien would have Ruby in a heartbeat, but Nora doesn't like to impose.'

'You seem to know an awful lot about my family. Are you friends with Nora?'

'Not really – she was three years above me in school.' Though what that had to do with anything, Gracie didn't rightly know. Gracie hadn't had many friends in school; she still didn't have many now, apart from Catrin. It was her own fault – she'd always preferred to stay in and sew, rather than go out and play or party.

'That makes you twenty-eight?' he guessed.

'Next month.'

'Happy next month birthday.'

'Thanks. Does that mean you won't be around for it?' Gracie thought it was a clever way of trying to discover how long he'd be staying in Applewell without asking him directly.

'Why? Would you like me to be? Are you having a party?'

'Good grief, no!'

'No, you don't want me to be, or no, you're not having a party?' He was smiling at her, his lips quirking more to one side than the other. 'Or perhaps you mean both?' he asked.

'I don't mean anything.'

He cocked an eyebrow.

She shook her head firmly. 'No party.'

'I don't like parties, either,' he said.

'You don't?'

'Can't stand a fuss.'

'How old are *you*?' This conversation was becoming increasingly bizarre.

'Thirty-four. I'd have thought you'd know that.'

'No one—' She stopped abruptly, mortified at what she'd been about to say.

'Mentions me?' he filled in, wryly.

'Not until recently.'

'I suppose it's to be expected.' He pulled a face. 'I'd better let you get on. I've taken up enough of your time. Thanks for the advice.'

'Any time.' Gracie was sorry to see him leave. The shop seemed considerably smaller without him in it, and she felt a sudden twinge of loneliness.

How absurd! Her shop was smack bang in the middle of the main street and scores of people wandered up and down it. Gracie was in her refuge, the place she loved the most, doing the thing she loved the most.

But when she picked up the quilt she was working on, for some reason her heart wasn't in it, and she put it back down again. Instead of the fat quarters she'd been cutting out of various oddments of fabric, her mind was on a good-looking face and the man it belonged to.

Chapter 9

Lucas

Lucas had no idea what peonies were but Gracie had suggested them so that was what he asked for.

The woman who was serving him said, 'Would you like some snapdragons in with it? They go nicely together. And what about some freesias and greenbells?'

Lucas had no idea what those were, either. 'Whatever you think is best,' he told the florist. 'In fact, make that two bunches.'

'You want two *bouquets*?'

'Yes, please.'

'You're Vivien's son, aren't you?' The woman looked at him from under a heavy fringe as she selected various blooms from a bucket at her feet.

'Yes, I am.' He briefly considered having a sign around his neck, so people wouldn't need to ask.

'Glad to be back?'

'Um, yeah.' Those two questions seemed to go hand in hand. He was far more confident answering the first, than he was the second.

'Bet your mum is pleased.'

'She is,' he agreed. 'Those are for her.' He indicated the flowers.

'Lucky her. The other bouquet is for Nora, is it?'

'Not really.'

The florist sent him a narrow-eyed look, but at least she didn't pursue the matter, because he would probably have told her to mind her own business and he didn't want to upset her. After all, his mother had to live here after he returned to London, and he didn't want to make it awkward for her – especially considering how much of an effort she'd made to show people how proud she was of him. That banner still made him shudder.

Lucas handed over his card to pay, then popped the doll into the bucket, along with the spade, and slipped the bucket's handle over his wrist, before picking up the bunches (he corrected himself, *bouquets*) and balancing them both in the crook of his arm. He certainly wouldn't be inconspicuous carrying this lot. Luckily, the bakers where his mum worked was further down the road, so he could slip off home without her seeing him – he wanted the flowers to be a surprise for her when she came home.

First, though, there was something he wanted to do.

The little bell above the door tinkled charmingly as he walked into A Stitch in Time for the second time that morning, but Gracie wasn't in her usual position near the window. In fact, she was nowhere to be seen.

'Hello?' he called and jumped a mile when a disembodied voice said, 'Hi.'

It seemed to be coming from the general direction of his feet and when he looked down he saw Gracie on her hands and knees underneath a table, picking up pins.

'Dropped them,' she said indistinctly, as she had several of them in her mouth, and he winced, thinking how painful it might be if she happened to jab herself with one.

She was holding a metal tin and she put the pins she had collected into it, before plucking the ones out of her mouth and popping those in, too. Then she rose gracefully to her feet.

'Those are beautiful,' she said. 'Vivien will love them.'

'Here.' He gently lifted one of the bouquets and handed it to her.

'You got two,' she said, taking it with a slight frown.

'That one is for you.' He gestured to the one she was holding.

'For *me*?'

'Yep, for you.'

'But...' Confusion was written all over her face: she looked like a concerned kitten.

'But what? I wanted to thank you for being so helpful,' he said, chasing the thought out of his head – why he kept comparing her to small, cute cats was beyond him.

Her eyes were huge as she stared at them, and she dipped her head to bury her nose in the petals. He couldn't tell whether she was pleased or cross.

'No one has ever bought me flowers before,' she said, somewhat indistinctly.

'Oh.' He didn't know what to say. He would have thought an attractive woman such as she would have received loads of bunches of flowers.

'Are they an early birthday present?' she asked.

'No, they aren't for your birthday.'

Gracie closed her eyes and sniffed the blooms, inhaling their scent with a blissful look on her face. Lucas was fascinated by the shape of her lips as she smiled softly, the curve of her cheek and the creamy texture of her skin, the faint blue veins on her eyelids—

'I can't accept them.' Her gaze locked onto his as she raised her head.

'Why not—' he began, then, 'Sorry, I didn't think. Your husband wouldn't like it.' He winced at his faux pas.

'I haven't got a husband,' she said.

'Boyfriend, then.'

'No boyfriend.'

'So, why—?'

'You should be giving these to Catrin,' she interrupted, thrusting them back into his arms.

He shoved them back at her. 'Why should I do that?'

'Because you upset her.'

'Not enough to give her flowers. And it wasn't me who upset her – it was whoever started the rumour that she was going to lose her job.'

Gracie tried to hand them back again, but Lucas danced out of reach.

'I still think you should give them to her,' she argued.

'Is there any reason why you can't accept them – apart from thinking I should gift them to a woman who has a partner and mightn't be at all happy that a strange man is giving her flowers?'

'They've split up.' Gracie caught her bottom lip between her teeth. Lucas couldn't take his eyes off her mouth.

'She did mention it, but I get the impression the split is very recent and she hopes it will be temporary. Besides, Catrin and I work for the same organisation and she happens to be rather junior to me in the scheme of things, so I don't think it's appropriate.'

'Now that you put it like that,' she said, 'my idea doesn't sound such a good one.'

'So you'll take them?'

'I don't deserve them. Give them to your mum.'

'I bought two bunches,' he reminded her.

'Give one of them to Nora.'

'I thought you told me I should offer to babysit?'

'I did.'

'Well, then. Please, accept the flowers. No strings, no ulterior motive. Just a simple thank you.' Did she think he was propositioning her? God, he hoped not. This was beginning to seem too much like hard work, and he was starting to wish he hadn't bothered.

She gazed at him steadily before making her decision. 'OK, thank you.' When she looked down at the flowers, a smile lit up her face.

Lucas felt an answering grin spreading across his own. Now that she'd allowed herself to accept them, her expression was one of delight, and it gave him a momentary twinge to think he was the person responsible for buying the first bunch of flowers she'd ever received. It made him itch to rush out and buy her another.

Curbing his enthusiasm, he said, 'I should go home and put these in water.'

'Why not give them to your mum now?'

'She's working,' he explained.

'I guessed as much. Vivien works most Saturdays.'

If Gracie knew that, why did she suggest he give them to her now? His puzzlement must have shown, because she said, 'She'll appreciate the gesture even more if you present them to her in front of her colleagues.'

'She will?'

Gracie nodded. 'Trust me.'

For Lucas trust didn't come easily, but to his amazement he found he did trust her.

–

'You shouldn't have,' Vivien said for the fourth time since arriving home from work, and she wasn't just referring to the bouquet – although he'd never seen her so thrilled as she'd been when he'd popped into the bakers this morning and had presented them to her with a flourish.

Gracie had been right. The gesture *had* meant a great deal to her.

Feeling rather better about himself than he'd done in a while (who knew the simple act of giving someone flowers could be so rewarding?) Lucas had decided to make the meal this evening. He was a decent enough cook – not accomplished but he got by – and he enjoyed the process, not even minding the washing up afterwards.

'I was going to make us something when I came in,' his mum said. She seemed rather put out. 'I don't expect you to cook.'

Too late it occurred to him that she might consider him to be a guest in her house. 'Sorry, I didn't mean to overstep the mark and take over your kitchen.'

'It's your kitchen, too.'

'Is it?'

'This will always be your home, no matter what.' Her voice was small and unshed tears glistened in her eyes.

'Oh, Mum.' Lucas had never been a touchy-feely person, and apart from that one hug when he'd first arrived home there hadn't been much physical contact since. But seeing her so upset cut him to the quick, and he covered the short distance between them and hugged her to him.

Sobs wracked her and she hugged him back, her embrace fierce. 'My son, my son,' she muttered, over and over, and he held her until she'd cried herself out, his soul aching with the knowledge that he was responsible for her pain.

Effron had been right – it *was* time Lucas came home and laid his demons to rest – and his friend's final words swam into his mind. Effron had asked Lucas how he could reconcile the empathy he felt for the homeless, with the lack of it that he'd displayed to his family over the years. Effron had guilt-tripped him into returning to Applewell. He'd made Lucas promise to go home. 'Your mother,' he'd said, 'deserves an explanation. She deserves an apology. But more than that, she deserves to know you love her and that she wasn't to blame for you running away.'

'I love you, Mum.' The words caught in his throat as his own tears threatened to fall. How could he have treated her so abysmally?

'I know, Luc, I know.'

Luc – no one except his mother had ever called him that. The nickname, together with the realisation that she knew he loved her no matter how negligent and remiss he'd been, was his undoing, and he finally gave in to the tears he'd been wanting to shed ever since he'd run away.

'Damn!' He leapt out of his mother's arms and sprinted across the kitchen.

Smoke was billowing out from under the grill, and he hastened to turn it off and rescue the steaks. Dismally he stared at the dried up, blackened lumps, and was about to apologise when the smoke alarm shrieked into life.

Lucas stared at his mum in dismay, seeing the shock on her face as she clapped her hands to her ears, then suddenly she was laughing and so was he. He laughed so hard, it brought fresh tears to his eyes. Or was that due to the smoke?

After opening both the front and the back door, plus all the windows, flapping a tea towel ineffectually in the air, and reassuring Mrs Hayworth, who'd hurried to check everything was all right, that he hadn't been trying to burn the house down and that she didn't need to call the fire brigade, the smoke alarm finally switched itself off.

'At least you know it works,' he said to his mother dryly. 'Sorry about dinner.' He seemed to have said sorry rather a lot today.

'Meh, it doesn't matter—'

'Where's the fire?' Nora demanded, charging into the house, her eyes wild.

'There isn't one,' Vivien said mildly.

'Flipping heck!' Nora put her hand on her chest. 'I had a phone call from Delia Green to say she saw smoke billowing from your house.'

'When anyone talks about smoke, they always say it's billowing.' Their mother closed the back door. 'I burnt some steaks.' She sent Lucas a look, warning him not to contradict her.

'So there isn't a fire?' Nora scanned the kitchen.

'No fire.'

'Thank God for that – I was about to phone Ianto.'

'I don't know if I told you, but Ianto is a fireman,' his mother said to Lucas.

Lucas was looking forward to meeting the guy who was his little sister's fiancé and his niece's father. Despite Lucas having come back to Applewell not long after Ruby was born, the two men hadn't bumped into each other. It might have had something to do with Lucas's visit being a flying one…

'Where's Ruby?' he asked.

'Delia's minding her.'

'You'd best get back to her,' Vivien said. 'As you can see, we're OK.'

'Have you been crying?' Nora demanded.

'It was the smoke. It stung a bit.'

'If it was that bad, shouldn't you get yourself checked out at the hospital? Smoke inhalation can be nasty.' Nora paused as she continued to look around. 'There doesn't appear to be any damage.'

'That's because there isn't. Now, go see to Ruby, while I try to find something else for tea.'

'If you're sure?'

Vivien shooed her away with her hands.

'Before you go, I've got a little present for Ruby,' Lucas said to his sister.

'From you?'

He nodded.

She followed him into the living room where he'd left the bucket and spade. When he handed them to her, Nora looked at them, her expression hard.

'I heard you bought Mum flowers,' she said, gazing at the vase on the sideboard at one end of the room.

Crumbs, word got around Applewell fast. 'Yes, I did.'

'I heard she was thrilled,' Nora continued. She held up the bucket and spade. 'You're not going to get around *me* as easily. Are you trying to salve your conscience?'

'No, I saw the bucket and thought—'

Nora leapt in, 'It might work on Mum, but it won't work on me. It'll take more than a cheap toy and a measly bunch of flowers for me to forgive you.'

Lucas hung his head. He deserved her ire. He welcomed it, in fact. His mother's forgiveness was far less easy to deal with.

'I heard you gave a bunch to Gracie Stewart, too,' she continued. 'Fancy her, do you?'

His head came up. 'Of course not! I, um—'

'Why? What's wrong with her?'

'Nothing! I just thought—' he changed tack '—she's been very helpful.'

'Hmph! I hope that's the only reason. Gracie is a lovely human being, and she doesn't need the likes of you swanning in and sweeping her off her feet.'

'I've no intention of—'

'Good! Are you going to give Catrin at UnderCover a bunch, too? Because I think you should. She's been really upset.'

'She had no reason to be.'

'She thought you were going to sack her.'

Lucas sighed wearily. 'I've absolutely no clue where she got that idea from.' Maybe he *should* take her some flowers, even though her being upset wasn't his fault.

'She must have got it from somewhere.' Nora's expression was accusing.

'Can I babysit for you some time?' he blurted.

'*What?* No, of course you can't. Ruby doesn't know you.' She scoffed at the offer.

'That's one of the reasons I'm here – I want to get to know my niece. And you.'

'If you hadn't run off and broken Mum's heart, you wouldn't need to get to know me or Ruby.'

'Are we really doing this now?' he asked, glancing towards the kitchen, conscious of their mother pottering around in there and probably listening to every word.

Nora hesitated, followed his glance, then shook her head. 'Come to mine later. Ianto will be at work. We can talk then.' Her tone was grim.

'OK.'

'Do you actually know where I live?'

To his shame, he didn't.

'We live on Oak Lane. Number fourteen. I'll see you at seven thirty. Don't be late.' And with that she was gone.

Lucas wasn't looking forward to this evening; not one little bit. But he had to go through with it if he wanted to rebuild his relationship with his sister – and he wanted that more than he'd wanted anything else in his life.

Chapter 10

Gracie

Never had a bouquet of flowers caused this much of a stir, Gracie marvelled, as she rooted around in a cupboard for something to put them in. She had a vase somewhere, one that she'd bought years ago for the daffodils she liked to treat herself to in the spring – they were such cheerful flowers. Ah, there it was.

She dug it out, gave it a rinse and filled it with water, and as she prepared the flowers for their new home, her thoughts drifted back to earlier in the day.

No sooner had Lucas left her shop, than Donald Mousel had come in (he'd never set foot inside the place before), pretending to have been sent in by Mrs Mousel to see if A Stitch in Time stocked tea towels.

It didn't, as Mrs Mousel well knew.

Then came Sid from the newsagent next door, on the pretext that he had been doing some stock rotation and had noticed he had some biscuits that were fast approaching their sell-by date and would she like a free packet?

Gracie knew for a fact that Sid usually discounted any items that were nearing their sell-by date, so she took an educated guess as to why he was here.

Neither man had asked her outright about the flowers Lucas had given her.

Mari Edwards, however, did. 'I hear Vivien's son bought two bouquets of flowers and gave one of them to you,' Mari had said.

Gracie had sighed. 'How do you know he gave one of them to me?' she'd asked.

'Eleri Jones had to pop to the butcher for some more bacon – she had a bit of a rush on full English breakfasts this morning – and she was just passing your shop when she saw him give them to you.'

'I see,' was all Gracie had said in the face of Mari's avid curiosity. 'How are you these days? You're getting about on your own now?' Mari had suffered a stroke a while ago and it had taken her some time to get back on her feet.

'Never mind me, what was Lucas Grainger doing giving you flowers? Are you courting?'

Gracie had burst out laughing. 'Definitely not! I only met him a couple of days ago.'

A couple of days ago or not, Gracie couldn't stop thinking about him, and with the flowers serving as a constant reminder, she wasn't likely to get him out of her head any time soon.

All done: Gracie stepped back to admire her handiwork. The bouquet was lovely, the flowers not quite in full bloom. It would be a day or so before all the buds opened and if she cared for them properly they might last a good ten days. She wanted to eek every drop of enjoyment from them because it would be a long time before anyone gave her another bunch.

For other people Saturday evenings were meant for going out for drinks, or for a meal, or to the cinema. For others, it was spent at home relaxing in front of the TV, often with friends or family. For Gracie, it was just another evening on the sofa with her sewing in her hands, and was no different from any other day of the week. She supposed she could pop to see her dad, but since he'd discovered online dating he was hardly ever at home. And when he was in, Gracie was worried he might be "busy". She'd dropped by once several weeks ago, and had been mortified and highly embarrassed to discover just how "busy" he'd been.

She hadn't paid him an unannounced visit since.

This evening, though, she was feeling restless and was finding it difficult to settle. She couldn't face trawling through Netflix trying to find something to catch her eye, and sewing failed to have its usual appeal.

Putting it to one side, Gracie decided to give him a call. Maybe she could pop in to visit him and pick up some fish and chips on the way. They could eat supper together: it was a while since they'd done that.

'Dad? It's Gracie. How are you?'

'Fab. I'm really fab.'

Fab? She'd never heard him say fab before. 'That's good. Are you doing—'

Before she could finish her sentence, her dad leapt in. 'Listen, love, I've got to run, I've got a hot date tonight.'

Hot date? Dear Lord! 'I see. That's… um… nice.'

'Her name is Ira, she's sixty and sexy.'

Good grief! 'I don't need to know that. Thanks, Dad.'

'I've bought some new aftershave for the occasion. Hugo Bod.'

'Boss, Dad.'

'Yeah, it *is* boss. I'll be bossing it.'

'That's not what I mea—'

'Gotta run. I'm in the kitchen in my underpants.'

'Eh?' Gracie had a vision in her head that she seriously didn't want to have. Despite knowing she shouldn't ask and hoping he'd pulled the roller blind down otherwise he'd give Miss Newbold next door a heart attack, she said, 'Why are you in your underpants in the kitchen?'

'Ironing my shirt.'

'Right… Hope you enjoy your date.'

'So do I, Gracie, love. So do I!'

Gracie stared at the screen for a moment before she put the phone down with a grimace. She didn't want to know about her dad's love life, or that his love life seemed far livelier than hers. Or that he was ironing his shirt in his underpants. Dear God…

Suddenly feeling incredibly lonely, she wandered into the kitchen, her tummy rumbling. She'd forgone lunch in Eleri's cafe today, not wanting to have to answer any more questions about Lucas Grainger and his flowers, so she was hungrier than usual for this time in the evening. But having chosen the relative calm of A Stitch in Time over Eleri's nosiness, she was now faced with having to make her own supper.

Unfortunately, there wasn't a great deal in her cupboards or her fridge, and what was there she didn't fancy eating. Or preparing.

An image of the chips that she had been hoping to tempt her dad with, sprang to mind, and once it was there it wouldn't shift. The image of those chips, liberally coated with salt and vinegar, was so vivid she could practically smell them.

Gracie fought it for as long as she could, even going as far as to pour some cereal into a bowl and stare mournfully at it, before she gave in to the inevitable and ventured out once more.

There was a queue in the chippie, as they were in the middle of frying a fresh batch of chips, which gave Gracie plenty of time to decide she simply must have a piece of fish, too. Or maybe a couple of those cod bites, which were essentially the same, only smaller and easier to eat with her fingers, because whilst she was waiting she made another decision – she'd eat her supper in the fresh air, and there was nowhere fresher and no view lovelier than the coastal path.

Fish and chips eventually bought, Gracie shoved the aromatic parcel under her jacket to keep it warm, popped the drink she'd bought to go with the food (because she'd need something to wash it down) into her pocket, and walked swiftly towards the edge of the village and the coastal path beyond.

At one end of the village was John Porter's farm and the path which stretched the length of the Welsh coastline, and at the other end was a small hidden cove. Both had their merits and she loved both equally, but this evening it was the cliffs that drew her, with their wheeling, raucous seabirds and the white-peaked waves of Cardigan Bay.

Gracie hurried along Oak Lane to reach the kissing gate which led to a path across John Porter's fields and followed the track until she came to another gate. Beyond it lay the coast path and the solitary splendour she'd chosen as her dining room this evening.

Finding a suitable rock not too close to the cliff edge, Gracie removed her supper from underneath her jacket and unwrapped it with a contented sigh. What more could she ask for? Good food, a breath-taking view, and not a soul in sight.

But as she ate, it wasn't the booming waves or the hopeful gulls that was on her mind, and neither was it the delicious chips and tasty fish. It was the lack of anyone to enjoy them with, and she suddenly wished that someone, anyone, would walk past so she didn't feel so utterly alone.

And for the love of all that was holy, why did she have an image in her head of who she'd like that person to be?

Damn Lucas and his bothersome bouquet. If it hadn't been for him, she'd have eaten in Eleri's cafe and she wouldn't be sitting here now, alone and melancholy, with his handsome face in her mind's eye.

Appetite gone, Gracie put down the chip she'd been holding. It didn't help that the salt which had been liberally sprinkled on it in the chip shop was being compounded by the tears plopping off the end of her nose as she bowed her head.

Sniffling, she scrunched up the remains of her supper and scrambled to her feet.

So much for enjoying a meal with a view.

All she'd done was highlight how lonely she was. There was nothing for it but to hurry back home – the sooner she had some sewing in her hands, the sooner she could pretend this evening had never happened.

Chapter 11

Lucas

Lucas was feeling distinctly out of sorts as he marched along Oak Lane. His mum, bless her, had whisked up a decent meal for them after his disastrous attempt, and they'd eaten it mostly in comfortable silence only interspersed with the occasional bland comment. But when he'd told her he was off out, she'd looked alarmed as he'd explained he was paying Nora a visit.

'It'll be fine,' he told her, hoping he was right.

His mother wasn't convinced. He didn't blame her – he wasn't, either. But he had to try, for all their sakes, especially for his mother's. She didn't deserve to have her children at logger-heads with each other, and he was hoping to appeal to Nora's better nature once he'd explained that to her. His sister might continue to hate him for what he'd put their mother through, but as long as she did so in private that was all he wanted. They all needed to play happy families at the wedding—

Actually, he didn't know whether he'd be welcome. Nora was getting wed in two months and he'd not received an invitation yet, so he was forced to admit that he might never receive one.

'Oh, hello.' Lucas, head down and stomping up the lane, had narrowly avoided bumping into Gracie, who was hurrying down it equally as fast.

She barely glanced up, but it was enough for him to catch a glimpse of reddened eyes and a stricken expression.

'Are you OK?' he asked.

'I'm fine.' She carried on walking.

Lucas hesitated, gave number fourteen a pained look, then turned smartly on his heel and sped after her. He couldn't let Gracie walk off when she was clearly upset.

Without thinking, he grabbed her arm as he caught up with her, hastily relinquishing his hold when she shook him off and glared at him.

'Sorry, I just...' He stuttered to a halt. 'You're not fine,' he observed.

'If I say I'm fine, I'm fine,' Gracie snapped.

'You don't look it.'

'I can't help the way I look.' She stared over his shoulder, refusing to meet his gaze. 'I'm *fine*.'

Lucas knew she wasn't; he'd had plenty of experience of people claiming they were OK when they so clearly weren't, and Gracie didn't fool him for a second. 'Can I do anything to help?'

'You've done enough,' she said, continuing to avoid his eye. She sniffed and a tear trickled down her face.

'What have I done?' Lucas was perplexed. He'd only spoken to the woman a handful of times, and one of those was to give her flowers. 'Is it the flowers? You told me you haven't got a husband or boyfriend.'

'I'm not lying.'

'I didn't say you were. If it's not that, what is it?'

'You wouldn't understand.'

'Try me.' He glanced behind, hoping Nora wasn't clock-watching. He was going to be late at this rate.

'I don't think so. Anyway, haven't you got somewhere to be?'

'Pardon?'

'Nora.' Gracie jerked her head in the direction of number fourteen.

See, this is what he meant by everyone knowing everyone else's business. He could try to refute Gracie's assumption and claim he was out for a walk, but she probably wouldn't believe him. 'I was only popping in for a quick visit. It can wait. Why don't you tell me what's wrong? I might be able to help.'

'I doubt that.' Another tear escaped and travelled slowly down her cheek. Lucas watched its progress and had an urge to brush it away.

She swallowed and moved away a step, and he knew he was about to lose her.

'Are you hurt?' he asked, trying a different tack.

Gracie barked out a joyless laugh. 'You could say that.'

'How? Where?' His gaze roamed over her as he tried to determine her injury.

'Here.' She slapped a hand to her chest.

'I don't understand.'

'Neither do I,' was her reply. 'Please leave me alone.'

'I want to help,' he insisted, surprised at how strongly he felt.

'You can't.'

'At least let me walk you back, to make sure you get home safely.' There was no way he was letting her walk home on her own in this state.

'No.'

'You can't stop me,' he said, with a gentle smile to show her he meant her no harm.

'I'll call the police.'

'Wouldn't it be easier just to let me escort you home? I've not got an ulterior motive – honest.'

Gracie uttered a bitter laugh. 'I didn't think you did.'

She turned on her heel and he fell into step alongside her. As they walked, he shot glances at her out of the corner of his eye, wondering what could have happened to make her so upset. If she had been one of the homeless in London, or in any other city, he could have hazarded a guess at cold, hunger, abuse, substance misuse or fear, to name but a few, and he could have attempted to do something about it.

Gracie, however, was a mystery.

'Don't look at me,' she warned.

'I wasn't.'

'You were.'

'OK, I was – but I was just checking you were all right.'

'I told you I was, didn't I?'

'Forgive me if I don't believe you; you're crying.'

'It's hay fever,' she retorted and stuck her nose in the air at his sceptical snort.

They carried on walking for several minutes more before she came to a halt outside a terraced house. 'This is me. You can go now.' She glared at him defiantly, daring him to linger.

Which made him want to linger all the more, even though he needed to be somewhere else; Nora would understand.

'I'll just wait until you're inside,' he said.

'I actually do live here, you know.' She huffed and pulled her keys out of her pocket, jangling them at him.

'I didn't suggest otherwise.'

'You did – why else are you still here?'

'To make sure you get home safely. I told you that.' Why didn't she believe him—? Ah, the flowers. He almost slapped a hand to his forehead; she must think he was coming onto her, and he didn't blame her. 'I'm not coming on to you, if that's what you think,' he said.

'So you keep saying. No need to rub it in.'

'Eh?'

She opened her front door, then faced him square on. Gosh, she was cute: a tiny but perfectly formed package compared to his great big lumbering form. He already thought her incredibly attractive, but she was downright gorgeous when she was cross. Tears had been replaced by flashing eyes, and the colour in her cheeks was no longer from crying but from temper.

'Leave me alone,' she said forcefully. 'I'm home, I'm safe – so go away.'

Lucas shook his head. 'Is that all the thanks I get?'

'Sod off. If you think you can walk me home without my permission and then expect payment in kind, you can think again.'

Lucas gaped at her. 'That's not what… I mean, I…' He threw his hands in the air – was there any point in trying to explain?

'Whatever.' She shot inside and slammed the door, making Lucas wince as it rattled in its frame.

He shook his head in disbelief. That she could think such a thing of him made his toes curl. He wasn't that kind of guy.

Whirling around, he strode along the pavement, once more heading towards Oak Lane, quietly seething.

Only when he opened the gate to his sister's cottage did he pause to look at the situation from Gracie's point of view. Her misconception had been his own fault. He'd expressed himself poorly, and it served him right if she thought badly of him.

To his surprise, though, he didn't want her to think of him that way. He wanted her to like him.

Why was that…?

–

'I said seven thirty. You're late.' Nora stood in the doorway, her arms folded across her chest, her mouth a firm line.

'I can explain.'

'Go tell it to the fairies.'

'Excuse me?'

'Ruby believes there are fairies at the bottom of the garden.'

'Right…'

'She talks to them.'

He opened his mouth, then closed it again.

'Well?' she demanded.

'Well, what?'

'What's your excuse?'

'I thought you wanted me to tell it to the fairies?' His lips twitched and he fought to stop them from breaking into a smile.

Nora poked her head out of the door and glanced up and down the lane. A curtain moved in one of the windows of the cottage next door. 'You'd better come in before the whole village sticks its nose in.' She pushed the door open with her hip, then turned and walked ahead of him. 'Make sure you close it behind you, else next door's cat will come in.'

He followed her into an open plan living-dining room, scanning it as he entered. 'You've got it nice,' he said, earning himself a sharp look.

'Did you think it would be a pigsty?' Nora shot at him.

'Not at all.' Crumbs, he couldn't say anything right.

His sister relented. 'If you'd seen it four months ago when we were in the middle of renovating it, then it was a pigsty. We bought it from Mari Edwards. She moved into the bungalow two doors up after she'd suffered a stroke.'

'Didn't that bungalow used to belong to the Nightingales?'

'Yep. They're dead now. Their son, George, came home to nurse old Mr Nightingale after Mrs Nightingale died. He's living next door up with a lovely lady called Nessa Millbrook. Anyway, this place was quite dated when we bought it. It needed rewiring and replastering, a new kitchen and— Hang on, why am I telling you all this? You haven't apologised for being late yet, and neither have you told me why you couldn't be bothered to be on time. I do have other things to do besides waiting around for you.'

'Sorry.' There he was again, apologising. It was all he seemed to be doing since he'd arrived. But then, what had he expected? 'I met Gracie in the lane and she seemed upset, so I made sure she got home safely.'

'What was she upset about?' Nora asked.

'No idea. She wouldn't tell me.' The whole encounter had been quite strange.

'She's a bit of an odd-bod, that one. Keeps herself to herself. I think she's shy.'

'I think she's lovely,' Lucas said without thinking

Nora drew herself up and folded her arms. 'Don't you go getting any ideas about Gracie. She's too nice for the likes of you.'

'Ouch. I deserved that.' He took a breath – this was why he was here, so he might as well get it over with. 'I'm not all bad, you know.'

'Just mostly.'

'Perhaps.'

They stared at each other for a moment.

'Where's Ruby?' he asked, and not just to break the silence. He was disappointed not to see her.

'In bed.'

'Oh.'

'You thought she'd still be up?'

Lucas shrugged.

'She's three years old. Her bedtime is at seven. You don't know the first thing about kids, do you?'

'Did she like her doll and the bucket and spade?'

'I haven't given them to her yet. I thought you might like to do that.'

Lucas sighed softly. 'I'd like that very much.'

'Not now,' Nora warned. 'She's asleep.'

'And you want to make sure I'm not going to run out on Mum again. Or you.' He knew his observation was spot on, and he didn't hold it against her. It would take time for her to trust him. Maybe if it had just been Nora, she'd be less prickly, but she had her daughter to consider.

'Fancy a beer?' Nora asked, and he sensed her softening a little.

'Are you having one?'

'I think I'm going to need one.'

'I didn't come back to upset anyone.'

'Yet you managed to anyway.' Nora took two brown stubby bottles out of the fridge and put one of them on the counter. She popped the top of the other and handed it to him, then did the same with hers. He watched her take a long draught.

'She'd have been more upset if I'd stayed away,' Lucas pointed out, leaning against a cupboard, the bottle cold in his hand.

Nora gazed at him over the top of hers, before tipping it up and taking another mouthful. 'You can't do right for doing wrong, can you? You should never have put Mum through it in the first place.'

She was right – he shouldn't have. But he had and he couldn't turn the clock back, no matter how much he wished he could. 'It's done. There's nothing I can do about that. All I can do now is to try to make it up to her.'

Nora snorted. 'You'll never do that.'

'It won't stop me trying.'

'Why now? Why after all this time? Do you know what it was like after you ran away? Can you even take a guess?' She shook her head and he saw tears gathering in her eyes. 'It was awful. She thought it was something she'd done or hadn't done, or something someone had done to you... She blamed herself and no matter how many times you tell her different, she always will. Why did you do it?'

Lucas sank half the contents of the bottle before he replied. 'I was young and stupid, and thought I could make it on my own.'

'Yeah, you and almost every other teenager on the planet – but most of them don't run away and put their families through hell.'

'I've got no excuse.'

'At least you phoned her.' Nora's voice dripped with scorn. 'It could have been worse. Those first few weeks when she didn't know whether you were alive or dead...' She shuddered, and brushed her tears away with an angry, impatient hand.

Lucas, to his eternal regret, had only phoned because Effron had forced him to call. Lucas, too full of shame, remorse, and plain old fear to face his mother's hurt, wouldn't have contacted her at all. As it was, the call had been brief, just a couple of words to let her know he was OK. He hadn't even told her where he was...

'It was seven years before you bothered to come and see her. Seven long years. How can you live with yourself?'

83

'I can't.' He swallowed, his throat and eyes burning.

'Will you go back to London?'

'I have to. I live there, my job is there.'

'How long will you stay away next time?'

'Not long.'

'I don't believe you.'

'Why should you? I've been a terrible son, a terrible brother. And I'm not much cop as an uncle either.'

'We should have had this conversation years ago.'

'Yes, we should.'

'Why didn't we?' Nora asked. She'd finished her beer and was making inroads into her second. Lucas thought he'd better stick to just the one.

'Because I was scared and a coward, and Mum was so pleased to see me whenever I came home. You weren't though.'

'I knew I'd have to pick up the pieces when you left again. It might have been better if you'd stayed away. Every time you paid her one of your fleeting visits, it took her weeks to return to normal. If you could call it normal. I remember how she was before you left.'

'I can't say or do anything to change the past. God knows, I wish I could. All I can do is try to make it up to her.'

'What if you can't?'

'That's the cross I'll have to bear. It won't stop me from trying.'

'You say that, yet you'll go back to London and it'll be months or years before we see you again.'

'It won't, I promise.'

She shot him a disbelieving look.

'I can't tell you I'm back for good, because I'm not. But I will be staying for a few weeks and when I go, I give you my word I won't stay away for long. I want to get to know my niece, for one thing, and for another I have a wedding to go to.' He gave Nora a small smile. 'Am I invited?'

She pursed her lips. 'I suppose you'd better come otherwise people will talk, and we've had enough of that to last us a lifetime.'

'Tell me about Ruby?'

Nora looked surprised, then her features softened. 'She's the best thing that's ever happened to me.'

'Better than winning that gymnastics competition when you were nine?'

'You remember that?'

He remembered everything. He'd spent hours and hours thinking of home, and trying to recall every single detail, dredging up memories he'd thought he'd lost. Some nights they had been the only thing keeping him warm.

'She's funny and sassy, and bossy,' Nora continued. 'And she's sweet and loving, and has an awful temper.'

'She sounds like you when you were her age. She looks like you, too.'

Nora blinked rapidly and looked anywhere other than at him.

'Can I see her? I promise I'll be quiet and not wake her.' Lucas shuffled from foot to foot, praying she'd say yes.

Nora said nothing for a good long while and Lucas was certain she was about to refuse, when she said, 'Come on,' and led him upstairs.

She pushed at a half-open door and peeped inside.

Lucas held his breath.

'Go on in,' she said, moving to the side to allow him to get past.

Lucas exhaled slowly, crept into the room and gazed down at his slumbering niece. In the dimness he could see dark lashes on plump cheeks, and her rosebud mouth was pursed. One hand was curled into a fist by the side of her head.

She was the most adorable thing he'd ever set eyes on, and he feasted on the sight of her, his heart constricting with an intense love he didn't know he was capable of.

He'd met Ruby before, but Nora had always been careful to keep her daughter at arm's length from him. He'd never even held her.

Watching her sleep was such a trusting and intimate thing, that he felt like weeping.

'I missed you,' Nora whispered, and he knew the admission cost her dearly.

'I missed you, too,' he replied, his voice low.

'Then why the hell didn't you just come home?' she hissed, her mood changing to anger as she ushered him out of the room and down the stairs.

'Because I didn't want to face what I'd done. I didn't want to admit that I'd made a mistake and have everyone laugh at me. I didn't want to come back until I'd made something of myself.'

'And have you?' She marched them back into the kitchen and picked up her half-drunk beer.

'Probably not.'

'You've never said what you do exactly. I know you're some kind of a big shot with UnderCover, but what do you *do*?'

'I'm not a big shot, honestly. I'm a Philanthropy Manager.' He caught her puzzled look. 'Yeah, no one knows what that is. Basically, I appeal to people's better natures to try to get them to donate money, time, or whatever else they can, to the charity.'

'Like one of the tin rattlers outside a supermarket?'

'Yes, essentially, but I target specific people, companies, or organisations.'

'What sort of people?'

'Wealthy ones.'

'Celebrities?'

'Sometimes. Business people more often than not.'

'You just knock on their door, or call them up and ask them for money?'

If only it were that simple. 'Kind of.'

He had to wine and dine, attend functions and parties just to get close to those whom he hoped to rally to the cause. He had to speak to their aides, their "people", their agents – anyone who could arrange a meeting or persuade them to put a hand in their pocket or champion the charity.

At first and for a few years, he'd loved the thrill of the chase, of hunting down someone who might be prepared to dip their hands in their deep pockets and give a small portion of their wealth to help those far less fortunate than themselves. Gradually, though, the longer he did the job, the more disillusioned he'd become. The vast divide between those he begged money from and those who had nothing, had slowly started to sicken him, to eat at him from the inside out until he wasn't able to do it anymore. And then Effron had died, years before he should have done, worn out by a lifetime of hardship and the inability to let anyone, including Lucas, take care of him.

His death had affected Lucas deeply. And, combined with his disillusionment, he'd had what he could only describe as a breakdown. Jonas had argued that Lucas had been working too hard and should take a holiday, go and enjoy himself for a couple of weeks somewhere hot with a beach and palm trees.

Instead, Lucas had returned to Applewell. He'd had a promise to keep.

Chapter 12

Gracie

Thank God it was Monday and the interminable Sunday was finally over, Gracie thought, as she headed into the heart of the village. Some shops and businesses in Applewell opened on Sundays and Gracie was beginning to regret that she hadn't opened A Stitch in Time yesterday. The day had been a long-drawn-out affair of doing chores that didn't need doing and watching TV she had no interest in.

She'd even broken her self-imposed rule of not doing any sewing for the shop at home, and had begun making small bowls out of coiled lengths of cord. She had a couple on her sewing desk to hold bobbins and buttons, so she thought she'd make some for the shop, having accumulated several pieces of cord from hoodies, pyjama bottoms and the like.

Four bowls later and still feeling out-of-sorts, she'd started work on a new quilt, hoping that by focusing on its design, she'd keep her mind away from the man she'd met on Oak Lane on Saturday evening. Trust her to run into the very person she didn't want to see. He'd only been in Applewell five minutes and was already making waves. Maybe he'd go back to London shortly and leave her in peace.

Dear Lord, no sooner had she thought of him, than there he was, strolling down the street without a care in the world. Hastily Gracie darted into the nearest doorway. Unfortunately it belonged to the bakery, and who should be working there but Lucas's mother. Great – everywhere Gracie turned he was there, mentally if not physically.

Oh damn, he was in here *physically too*, she realised, as he followed her inside.

'What can I get you?' Vivien asked, and Gracie's panicked eyes shot to her as she fished around for something to say. 'Are you OK?' Vivien's face was full of concern.

'I don't think she is,' Lucas said, coming closer and peering at her. 'She was a bit upset on Saturday evening.'

'She was? You didn't say anything about meeting Gracie on Saturday. You told me you'd gone to our Nora's. You didn't mention you'd been anywhere else.' Vivien gave her son a curious look, then turned her attention back to Gracie, who wished everyone would butt out and go away.

'I didn't go anywhere else,' Lucas said. 'I met Gracie on the way to Nora's and she seemed upset, that's all.'

'What's wrong, dear?' Vivien asked, directing the question to Gracie who wanted nothing more than to disappear.

'I'm fine. Can I have an Eccles cake, please?' She pointed at the first thing she set eyes on.

'Just the one?' Vivien was looking at Lucas then back to her again.

'Just the one,' Gracie confirmed, rather more forcefully than she'd intended.

'Crumbs, I haven't had an Eccles cake in years,' Lucas said. 'I think I'll have one as well.'

'Shall I put them in the same bag?' Vivien asked.

'No! Definitely not.' Gracie glared at her, then she glared at Lucas. And she continued to glare at everyone and everything until she had paid and was hurrying across the road to her own little shop.

It was only when she reached A Stitch in Time and was digging around in her bag for her keys, that she realised Lucas was right behind her. With a squeak, she fumbled and dropped them. They fell to the pavement with a clatter, and as she made a grab for them the Eccles cake slipped from her grasp and slid out of its paper bag, landing on the ground in a splatter of flaky pastry.

'Now look what you made me do!' she cried, wringing her hands.

Lucas bent down to retrieve her keys and sweep the cake back into the bag, before handing both to her. Gracie stared at the bag, then stared at Lucas.

'I'm not eating that,' she said. 'It's been on the ground.'

'I didn't expect you to. I was hoping you'd put it in the bin. I didn't want anyone to step on it and make a mess.'

'Oh, yes, OK, that's what I'm going to do with it. Right now.' Gracie stuck her nose in the air. 'If you'll excuse me.' She shuffled past him and jabbed the key in the lock.

To her immense annoyance as soon as she pushed the door open, he followed her in and stood there until she'd disabled the alarm and switched on the lights.

'Can I help you?' she demanded, throwing the spoilt pastry in the bin and her bag on the counter. The latter landed with a heavy thud and she winced, hoping she hadn't damaged the bowls she'd made yesterday.

Wordlessly, Lucas held out the bag with his own Eccles cake in it.

Gracie ignored it. She wished she could also ignore the man who was holding it, but he was standing in the middle of her shop, making it look small and crowded.

'What do you want?' she asked.

'I want to know you're OK.'

'I'm fine.'

'No, you're not.'

'How would you know? You don't know me or anything about me.'

'I'd like to.' He stopped abruptly and surprise flitted across his face.

Gracie turned away in disgust. 'Mind the step on the way out,' she said, and she didn't turn around again until long after the little bell had tinkled.

'Arggh!' Her scream was so loud it was a wonder the whole village didn't hear it. 'You're still here! Why?!' She couldn't believe he'd allowed her to think he'd left. What a sneaky—!

'Because I think you need a friend.' Lucas was leaning against the door, his arms folded, preventing anyone from entering.

'I've got a friend. Plenty of friends,' she added quickly. 'I don't need another one.' *Especially not one as attractive as you*, she thought to herself. And especially not one who will soon be going back to where he'd come from. She didn't need a friend like that.

'They'll get it out of you, you realise.' He was smiling wryly, a gentle twist of the lips.

'They won't.' She was adamant. 'There is nothing for them to get out.' It was no secret that she was shy and introverted – everyone in Applewell knew this and they respected her wish for space and solitude. Except this guy. She enjoyed the banter with her customers in the shop (or at least, she tried to), and she enjoyed a chat with people she knew. But she also enjoyed her own company, maybe too much sometimes, but that was how she liked it. Who was this man to try to muscle in on her life?

Gracie pushed away the memory of how lonely she'd felt on Saturday evening sitting on the cliffs and eating her solitary supper. Every now and again she'd feel sorry for herself or wish that things were different, but everyone felt like that on occasion. She'd get over it. Heck, she already had, because she certainly didn't feel lonely right now.

'They're all-knowing and all-powerful,' he said. 'You can't keep any secrets from them.'

'By "them", I'm assuming you mean the kind and generous people of Applewell?' Her tone was sarcastic, but she wasn't going to apologise for that. Just who did he think he was, making judgements about Applewell when he hadn't set foot in the place for years, except for the occasional flying visit lasting only a couple of hours: she'd been filled in by Catrin, who'd gotten the story from Eleri.

'Yes, they are kind and generous,' he agreed.

'Is that why you ran away? Because of all that kindness and generosity?' she asked, then bit her lip. That was so rude of her, and she felt a total heel when his face closed up and hurt flashed in his eyes.

'I ran away because I was young and stupid, and thought I knew everything.' He straightened. 'You know where I am if you want a chat. I'm not the ogre everyone believes me to be.' He looked sad.

Dismayed to think she was the cause, she said quietly, 'I don't think you're an ogre.'

He hesitated, his hand on the door handle.

'I think you're nice,' she added for good measure.

'Nice?' His lips twitched.

'Yes, nice.' Gracie warmed to her theme. 'Considerate, too.' A blush bloomed in her cheeks and she cursed herself for feeling sorry for him. She didn't even know why she'd said he was nice. As she'd just told him, he didn't know anything about her, and the sentiment went the other way – she knew nothing about him and had no idea whether he was nice or not. She suspected not, after what he'd put his mother through.

But something told her she was being unfair and she should give him a chance – or the benefit of the doubt, at the very least.

'Is that Eccles cake still on offer?' she asked.

He considered her question for longer than it warranted. 'It is,' he replied slowly.

'I'll put the kettle on. We can go halfsies.'

'Halfsies? I haven't heard that expression in ages.' He smiled. 'I can always nip across the road and get another one?'

Gracie was horrified. 'Please don't. There's enough talk as it is.'

'About what?' He trailed after her as she walked into the room at the back where she kept a kettle, a tabletop fridge and a couple of mugs.

'The flowers,' she replied in an ominous tone.

'What about them?'

'Everyone's talking about you giving me flowers.'

'Everyone?'

She nodded, plugging the kettle in and switching it on. 'That's why you saw me on Oak Lane on Saturday.'

Lucas was clearly baffled. He squinted at her and tilted his head to one side, like a confused spaniel.

Gracie sighed. She'd gone this far, so she may as well tell him the rest. Not all of it, of course, not the silly reason she'd been crying. 'So many people came into the shop wanting to know why you'd given me flowers that I couldn't face going to Eleri's cafe for lunch. Which meant I was hungry when I got home, and as I didn't have much in the house, I treated myself to fish and chips and went to the cliffs to eat it.'

'That doesn't explain why you were crying.'

'You don't give up, do you?'

'Nope.'

'Tea or coffee? I've only got instant, I'm afraid.'

'Instant will do.'

'Milk?'

'Yes, please.'

She made the drinks, then popped the Eccles cake on a plate and cut it in half. She took one of the pieces and gave the plate with the remaining portion to him. Cupping a hand under the pastry, she took a bite.

'You still haven't told me why you were crying,' he persisted.

'It doesn't matter. It's no biggie,' she said, somewhat indistinctly through a mouthful of sweet stickiness and flaky goodness.

'It matters to me.' He was gazing at her, and once again Gracie felt heat flood her cheeks.

'I don't want to talk about it,' she said firmly. And thankfully he backed off. There was a fine line between caring, being downright nosey and being rudely persistent, and he was perilously close to the latter.

'Have the cliffs altered much?' he asked, and she was relieved that he'd changed the subject.

'Not at all. Still as cliffy as they were when you were a kid.'

'How about the cove? Has it been invaded by tourists?'

Gracie smiled. 'Not yet. The path down to it is overgrown and it's not signposted or anything.'

'I used to love it there.'

'I still do. When I need a break from sewing that's where I usually go.'

'Care to come for a walk with me?'

'Pardon?'

'Not today, obviously, because you're working, but how about on your next day off.'

'That's not until Sunday.'

'I don't mind waiting. I'm not going anywhere.' He paused, then amended it by saying, 'For a while.'

To her surprise, Gracie fancied the idea. It would make a change not to spend Sunday on her own, and although the walk would only take a couple of hours at the most (and that was if they dawdled) it would get her out of the house and away from her sewing. It would do her good.

'I'd like that,' she said, shyly.

'Great.' He finished his coffee and put his mug down. 'It's a date.'

Only after he'd left, having made arrangements for him to pick her up at her house, did Gracie wonder if it had just been a turn of phrase, or whether she really was going on a date.

Chapter 13

Lucas

He couldn't mope around all day doing nothing – he'd die of boredom by the end of the first week – and he had promised Jonas that he'd do some work, yet neither was he in the right frame of mind to make begging calls. With the mood he'd been in since Effron had passed away, the tone of any phone call would end up being along the lines of 'just give Under-Cover some money and stop making me jump through hoops', followed by 'you've got too much of it anyway'. At least with an email he could vet and temper what he wrote, before pressing the send button. But even then he was reluctant to begin the predictable to-ing and fro-ing which was needed to squeeze a drop of funds out of whoever it was he was trying to persuade to donate.

He didn't resent the wealthy or the influential – many of them had worked damned hard to get where they were. What he resented was a society that paid footballers, actors and reality TV stars huge amounts of money whilst other people didn't have a roof over their heads.

Last night after he'd returned from Nora's house, he'd watched a programme on the telly where a restaurant in the US charged $5000 for a beefburger. *$5000!* And anyone who was daft enough to pay that kind of money for a patty of meat in a bread roll got a certificate to prove it. It was obscene, that's what it was. He'd had to switch channels because the programme had made his blood boil.

He couldn't do anything to change society, but he could do something to help the homeless. Not all of them, obviously, but he did what he could, when he could. It wasn't enough (it would never be enough) but he did his best.

Unfortunately, his best seemed to have deserted him lately, which was one of the reasons he'd found himself back in Applewell.

After his Eccles cake encounter with Gracie, he decided to pop into UnderCover. Maybe he could make himself useful there and sort donations out, or price goods up. He'd been serious when he'd said he wanted to see what could be done to maximise profits. The shops ran on a shoestring as it was, and he wasn't looking to make employees redundant or close outlets down: what he wanted to do was to explore other ways of generating income from what they already had. He was sick of having to beg and plead with the rich and famous. It was sensible to start at the grassroots of the charity – the shops – where ordinary people were helping to raise money for the homeless.

Catrin wasn't exactly pleased to see him, but when he explained he was only there to help, she relented a little.

'I'm a pair of hands short,' she told him. 'Mrs Hayworth usually volunteers on a Monday but she's feeling under the weather, so she won't be in today.'

'Would there normally be just the two of you?' He couldn't see anyone else in the shop.

Catrin nodded. 'Except Wednesdays when there are three people in, but not all at once. Wednesday is my day off, you see. You can make a start on those, if you want.'

'Those' were three black plastic bags on the floor by the counter. Lucas untied the nearest and peered inside. It was full of clothes, mostly, and a board game, and he could see one shoe but not the other, so he hoped it was lurking at the bottom of the bag.

'They were left outside. I found them there this morning,' Catrin said.

'Does that happen a lot?'

'All the time. Sometimes they've been picked over, and people have taken what they fancy. Other times, such as bank holidays, bags end up staying outside for a couple of days, and that's not great when the weather is bad.'

Lucas wasn't sure what, if anything, could be done about the problem, so he shelved it to think about later. No doubt other staff in Head Office with more experience of how the retail side of the charity ran would have already considered the issue. Lucas had worked his way up via a different route (the shelters and the soup kitchens) so he found this side of the charity fascinating.

He began taking things out of the bag, wondering how they should be sorted.

'Check for wearability first,' Catrin advised, seeing his uncertainty. 'If it's got buttons missing, or the zips don't work, or it's only one of a pair, or has holes, tears, or stains,' she shuddered, 'put it to one side. Everything else needs to be labelled, and the clothes have to be hung on a hanger, given a size cube, then steam cleaned. Only then is it ready to go on the shop floor, and sometimes not even then.'

Lucas frowned. 'Why not?'

'If it's December, you don't want to be putting summer dresses out, and you don't want to be displaying fleece-lined boots in the middle of June.'

'That makes sense.'

'There's a supply of hangers out the back, and baskets of size cubes.' Catrin showed him what she meant, taking a plastic cube off a hanger and slipping it back on again. 'Here's a price guide – if there's anything you're not sure about just ask. And when you've done that, I'll show you how to use the steamer.'

'What about things like this?' Lucas held up a red woollen coat with the sleeve hanging off. If it wasn't for the seam at the shoulder having been torn, the coat was in really good condition.

'That'll have to go in the bin out the back,' she said.

'You're not going to throw it away, are you?' He was fairly certain that the charity used a textile recycling service, having seen some emails mentioning it a couple of years ago. He hadn't taken much notice at the time because he'd been more interested in getting local supermarkets to donate unsold food to their nearest soup kitchen. UnderCover didn't rely solely on the shops or his efforts to persuade people to part with their money – there were many more sides to the organisation – and limiting waste had always been a cause close to his heart. This stint in one of the shops was fascinating, though.

'Um, no, they are, um, recycled. That's what the bin is for.' Catrin had her back to him as she tidied a rail and he could see she was busy, so he got on with his own task. There'd be plenty of time to ask questions over the next few weeks.

After sorting through the bags and picking out the things he didn't feel were saleable, Lucas gathered them up and went out the back. Sure enough, he saw a large canvas trolley on wheels, the kind of thing a hotel or a hospital might use for laundry, with a few items in the bottom, which, when he checked them out were badly soiled. Feeling it to be a bit of a waste but glad that the charity was getting something for them at least, he dumped the coat and several other items into it and went back to the things that could be sold in the shop.

'Have you just had a collection?' he asked, referring to the bin. 'Or don't you get much in the way of damaged goods?'

'Erm…' Catrin began, but before she could say anything further, a customer asked her a question and her attention turned to the lady and the dress she was holding up.

Lucas found it extremely satisfying to spend the day doing something totally different from what he usually did. He found he enjoyed steam cleaning (who'd have thought it could be so immensely gratifying to watch the creases drop out of clothes), and he also loved chatting to customers, even if many of the people who came into the shop did so merely out of curiosity about him. It seemed he was still something of a sensation in

Applewell, and it surprised him that the villagers continued to be so interested.

At around one o'clock his stomach rumbled and his thoughts turned to food. 'What do you do about lunch?' he asked.

'Normally, I sit out the back for half an hour with my sandwiches, or I pop out for a bit. But I won't go out today – I wouldn't like to leave you on your own. It wouldn't be fair.'

'I can manage,' he insisted. 'Go and eat your lunch.'

'You haven't had yours yet,' she pointed out.

'I'll be OK for a while,' he said, then his stomach rumbled loudly again and Catrin giggled.

'Liar,' she said. 'Go and eat; I'll have mine after you've had yours.'

Lucas gave in – after all, Catrin was in charge of the shop and he'd meant it when he'd said he didn't want to tread on her toes.

Unlike Catrin, he hadn't brought anything with him, so he had a choice: buy something from the bakers (and risk his mum wanting to chat), pick up a sandwich from the little supermarket, or eat in Eleri's cafe.

He decided on the cafe, the lure of a proper cup of coffee proving too great. He could put up with instant for a while, but he was practically drooling at the thought of freshly ground beans. His one luxury was his coffee machine, and he briefly toyed with popping back to his London flat to fetch it, before deciding the idea was a bad one – if he went back, he'd end up staying, and he wasn't ready for that yet. He didn't want to upset his mum or get on Nora's bad side after working so hard to bring her round. His sister still didn't trust him, but with a great deal of effort on his part, she might. Rushing back to London when he'd promised to stay in Applewell for a few weeks wouldn't help. Besides, there was a trip to the cove in the offing. He hadn't been there since he was a teenager, and he was looking forward to it.

He was also looking forward to spending time with Gracie. Maybe she'd open up to him? Even if she didn't, he would have tried to get to the bottom of what troubled her.

That was the story he told himself – his anticipation had nothing to do with the fact that he found Gracie extremely attractive.

Chapter 14

Gracie

'What are you doing here?' Gracie asked. 'Is everything OK?'

Catrin glanced nervously up and down the street. She was holding two carrier bags.

'Is it Gareth? Has something happened?' Gracie asked, standing aside to let her friend into the house. It was eight o'clock on Thursday evening and Catrin didn't normally pop in after hours. They tended to do most of their socialising during the day, or on pre-arranged visits to the pub.

'Don't talk to me about that man,' Catrin growled. 'Here, these are for you.' She thrust the bags at her, and Gracie carried them into the house.

'Thanks, but I could have called into UnderCover for them. Not that I'm not pleased to see you,' she added hurriedly. 'Tea? Or would you prefer something stronger, and you can tell me all about he who shouldn't be named.'

'Gah! It's been over a week since he told me he wanted a "break".' Catrin used her fingers to make quotation marks in the air. 'Yet we're still living under the same roof. You'd think he'd have found somewhere else by now, even if it was a sofa in one of his mate's houses. Saying that though, they've all got wives and girlfriends who won't want a great big hairy bloke dossing in their living room.'

Gracie dropped the bags into the front room on her way to the kitchen. She'd take a look at the contents later. It was always such a thrill to root through the things Catrin gave her – she never knew what she was going to find.

Catrin followed, sinking down into a chair and resting her elbows on the kitchen table. She looked desolate, and Gracie's heart went out to her.

She took the wine out of the fridge, poured a glass and handed it to her. 'Here, get that down you.' She took a gulp of her own drink and slid into the seat opposite. 'It sounds to me like he's not really serious about the break thing.'

'I wish you were right, but I've hardly seen him since last Wednesday. He's either out or asleep in the spare room. What am I going to do, Gracie? How am I supposed to carry on without him?'

'Aw, love…' Gracie stood and put her arms around Catrin's shoulders.

She let her friend cry herself out before she resumed her seat, her heart breaking for her.

It must be so hard for Catrin, living in the same house as the man she loved, knowing that he didn't love her back. Gracie wanted to give him a piece of her mind, but even if she had the courage, she knew better than to interfere. Catrin and Gareth had to work this out between them. Gracie wished for her friend's sake that Gareth would hurry up and make up his mind either way, because this current situation was tearing her friend apart.

There was one thing she could do to help, however.

'Do you want to move in with me for a while? Until Gareth sorts himself out.'

'Bless you,' Catrin sniffed. 'Thanks for the offer, I really appreciate it, but I'm staying put.' There was a steely glint in her eye behind the brimming tears. 'He's the one who wants us to break up, so he's the one who should leave. Besides, if he's serious about "spreading his wings" then he'll be gone soon enough.'

She looked desolate at the thought and Gracie's heart squeezed.

'The horrible thing is, I can kind of see where he's coming from,' Catrin said, dabbing at her damp cheeks as her tears spilled over once more.

'What do you mean?' Catrin and Gareth were made for each other – they were perfect together. Gracie had always aspired to have the kind of relationship they had. Although Catrin and Gareth weren't married, they were as good as.

'We did get together too young. All we've known is each other and Applewell. Perhaps we should both broaden our horizons.'

Gracie inhaled sharply. 'Date other people, you mean?'

'No. Definitely not.' Catrin shook her head emphatically. 'If he wants to, I can't stop him; but I'm not interested. He's the only man for me and if I can't have him, I don't want anyone else. I'm talking about seeing a bit more of the world.'

'Where would you go? What would you do?'

'Not a clue.' Catrin gazed despondently into her wine glass, and Gracie had the distinct impression that Catrin's heart wasn't in this madcap idea of hers. 'The thing is, I'm not sure he wants to spread his wings in the sense of seeing more of the world. He just wants to not be with me.' Her face crumpled again and her chin wobbled. 'I thought we'd be together forever,' she wailed. 'What am I supposed to do without him?'

Gracie had no idea, either. It had never occurred to her that Catrin and Gareth would split up. Heck, she'd even planned what she'd wear to their wedding, assuming that the next step would be for Gareth to propose.

Their relationship had been one of the constants in her life. When she thought of love, she thought of them. When she imagined being in a romantic relationship herself, she prayed it would be as solid and as enduring as theirs.

With Catrin and Gareth splitting up, Gracie decided she might as well give up on love. If those two couldn't stay the course, there was no hope for anyone, let alone herself.

Gracie always, always found solace in sewing. Needle and thread had never let her down, and throughout the following day she sat by her shop window working on the new quilt in between customers, trying to take her mind off her friend's heartache. She wished she could do something to help her. The breakdown of Catrin's relationship with Gareth had rocked her to the core, so she did what she always did: she lost herself in her sewing.

This time though, when she closed the shop for the evening she didn't take her sewing home with her; she had those bags of things that Catrin had given her yesterday to go through, and it could take a while if she had to unpick zips and free linings from coats, or cut fabric up so that the damaged parts could be discarded. Catrin brought her everything and anything (apart from soiled items – yuck!) and Gracie was always excited to see what she'd got. She'd intended to get started last night, but after the pair of them had polished off the wine and Catrin had had yet another cry, Gracie had been too strung out to do anything other than retire to bed.

This evening, though, she was ready to do some sorting, so, with a cup of tea in her hand, she went into her front room. This used to be the room where she ran her business from until she'd made a leap of faith and had taken out the lease on the small shop next to the newsagents.

In some ways, her front room remained the hive of her business. It still contained a couple of sewing machines and an overlocker machine, plus a cutting table which dominated the small room and which she had to sidle around to get from one side of it to the other. One wall was lined with shelves on which sat baskets of thread and bobbins, assorted needles, pins, scissors, tailor's chalk and everything else a confirmed seamstress needed. And fabric – all shades, sizes, weights and patterns, all neatly folded.

This room, more than any other place, was where she was happiest.

It was a bit of a squeeze, but she had an armchair right by the window, and this was where she headed with her cup of tea and the bags from Catrin. Curling herself up in the seat, the window cranked open to let in some fresh air and the twittering of sparrows on the rooftops, she untied one of the bags and took the first thing out.

It was a T-shirt, freshly laundered by the smell of washing powder that clung to it, but with a dribble of what looked like bleach at the hem on the front. She could certainly use the fabric for something once she'd cut it up and discarded the bleached part. She'd return the damaged part, and any other bits she had no use for (although she could make use of most things) to Catrin for disposal in the fabric waste bin. According to Catrin, most charities who handled clothing and other textiles, had a collection service for items which couldn't be sold. More often than not, those items ended up abroad, where they were either sold on as they were, or were reprocessed into things like insulation, stuffing for mattresses, or underlay for carpets. What an item ended up being in its next incarnation depended very much on what it was made of – cotton-rich fabrics were often used to make rags used in industry because they absorbed moisture well, but some textiles, especially polyester, were incinerated.

Gracie hated the sheer waste of it, which was why she tried to use every scrap that came her way so that as little as possible had to be reprocessed, burnt, or sent to landfill. Her efforts might be insignificant in the bigger scheme of things, but if everyone was more mindful about what they did with their unwanted clothes, sheets, towels, curtains and so on, the world would be a better place as far as she was concerned.

Next was a black skirt made of a crimplene-type fabric that was so bobbled it was unwearable and unusable apart from the lining which Gracie carefully removed, the zip, which worked fine, and the button. The latter was added to her impressive collection. She reused jam and other jars to store them, and she had at least sixteen jars with assorted coloured buttons sitting on the shelf. She probably had more than she'd ever use in a lifetime, but she couldn't bring herself to throw any of them away.

As she worked, she thought of George Nightingale, who lived on Oak Lane. He never used to throw anything away in case it came in useful, but he'd taken it to the extreme and had become a bit of a hoarder. Gracie warned herself not to end up in the same boat as George, who had got to the point where his bungalow had become dangerous to live in. Lottie Hargreaves had a tendency to hang onto stuff as well – in her case it was bits of wood, hinges, door knobs, and anything else she could salvage in order to give discarded and damaged furniture a new lease of life.

Which reminded her, Gracie had yet to give the upholstery demonstration she'd promised Lottie in exchange for a Welsh dresser. Bartering was a slightly odd and old-fashioned way of doing things but it worked for Gracie, and at least she didn't have to declare the dresser or the lunches in Eleri's cafe she'd got in exchange for making cushions for the kiddie's corner, to the tax man!

A red coat was the last item in the bag, and Gracie examined it solemnly. A well-known make, it was heavy, good-quality fabric. Double-breasted and with a matching belt, it was a wool-mix and very smart – apart from the seam of one sleeve gaping open. The lining was intact, the damage only affecting the outer fabric, and it could easily be repaired. It was a shame to reduce it to its component parts when, with a little effort, it could be wearable once again. What had happened to it, she wondered, for the seam to have torn. What was its story? Gracie often tried to imagine the journey a garment had made before it came into her hands, and she wished she knew this one's history.

She examined it carefully for any other damage and, not finding any, she put it to one side. She'd repair it, she decided, and return it to UnderCover. She guessed the coat might have been quite expensive when it was new and the charity could ask a decent sum for it. It was the least she could do considering all the things Catrin had given her. Gracie often repaired items if she could, rather than taking them apart and making them into something new, and she'd lost count of the number of new zips she'd put into garments or the buttons she'd sewn back on. The arrangement suited both her and Catrin, as well as their respective businesses.

In fact, A Stitch in Time wouldn't exist without it.

Chapter 15

Lucas

Lucas had thought about giving himself a day off, but he was enjoying helping out in UnderCover so much that he worked six days straight. Catrin was getting a little antsy at his enthusiasm, and he decided that for her sake he should back off a little next week. He didn't want to fuel any more rumours that he was planning on being the shop's manager himself and doing Catrin out of a job. Things had settled down for him in Applewell; he no longer seemed to be the talk of the town and he wanted to keep it that way.

He decided to finish early today. There were enough volunteers, and he was surplus to requirements. It would be nice if he could persuade Catrin to leave early instead, but he doubted she'd be happy with his suggestion and once again he might run the risk of her getting the wrong end of the stick. He wanted to mull over a few things in any case, and his thought process would fare better away from the shop.

First though, he'd have a cup of coffee or three in Eleri's cafe before heading off home.

Home... It was telling that he still thought of the house he grew up in as home. Whenever he thought of his flat in London it didn't feel like home. He might say 'I'm going home now' after a hard day at the office, but it was merely a turn of phrase. Home wasn't his flat. Home was the place he'd left seventeen years ago and the one he was increasingly glad he'd returned to.

Catrin was in the stockroom when he went to tell her he had finished for the day. Sales had been consistent this morning and some of the rails were looking less full than usual, so he found her choosing things to put out on the shopfloor.

'More shorts?' he said, checking out what she had in her arms.

'It's the weather for it. We've already had two lots of tourists in from the campsite up the road who didn't expect it to be quite so sunny. I can't believe this spell of fine weather is lasting so long.'

'Need a hand?'

'I'm good, thanks.'

'I thought I'd shoot off early today, if you can manage.'

Catrin gave him a smile. It was nice to see. Although she was always bright and cheerful with the customers, behind the scenes her sadness showed. He didn't like to ask, but he guessed things still weren't great between her and her partner. She was looking very peaky and there were dark circles under her eyes. She seemed to have lost her appetite, as well, because he noticed she often only took a couple of bites out of her sandwiches before throwing the rest away. The situation at home was making her ill, and he wished he could do something to help.

'We managed before you came...' she said, leaving him to complete the rest of the sentence.

'I'll be off, then.'

'Going somewhere nice?'

Lucas's thoughts immediately went to his walk with Gracie tomorrow. 'I've got a couple of reports to write,' he said, then on seeing her panicked expression, he swiftly added, 'It's nothing to do with the shop. It's regarding the funds that have been raised by the other revenue streams of the charity.' Revenue streams which he should be working on right now, instead of swanning about in Applewell. But the thought of going back to his proper job made him feel cold and clammy, even though he was consumed by guilt.

Guilt was something he carried with him constantly – a bit more wasn't going to make a great deal of difference.

He was about to follow Catrin onto the shopfloor, when his gaze fell on the waste fabric bin and he paused. There hadn't been much in it to begin with, but there was even less now. Frowning, he moved closer and peered inside.

Strange... he couldn't see most of the things he'd put in there on Monday, or the majority of the stuff that had been placed in there since as other donations had come in and had been sorted.

He leant over and had a rummage, his frown deepening.

He vaguely remembered some of the items he'd thrown into it – a heavy-weight red winter coat in particular – but there was no sign of it or of any of the other things, apart from a rather nasty babygro that hadn't been washed before it had been donated. He recalled his horror when he'd taken it out of the bag and realised what the stains were.

What had happened to the rest, he wondered?

He decided to ask Catrin after he'd washed his hands, but when he returned to the sales floor she was admiring a dress a customer was trying on, and he guessed it could wait. There'd be a logical explanation, and one he needed to hear if he was to fully understand how the shops operated.

'You can't stay away, can you?' Eleri teased when he entered the cafe a few minutes later.

Lucas took a deep breath, inhaling the delicious aroma of freshly ground beans. Gosh, that smelt so darned good.

'The usual?' she asked.

He nodded. 'And could I have a ham and cheese panini to go with it?'

'Coming right up,' she said, and he headed for a free table.

It happened to be near the children's play area where two small humans were pretending to cook things, and he smiled as he watched them.

'You wouldn't believe that play kitchen used to be an old TV stand in a former life,' Eleri said, as she put his order on the table. 'Lottie Hargreaves – do you know her? No? Never mind... Lottie made it. Or rather, she showed me how to do it myself, with some help from her. She runs courses in upcycling. And your friend Gracie made the cushions on those seats. She's single, by the way. Is there anything else I can get you?'

'No thanks.'

He already knew Gracie was single, but as they weren't going on a date her relationship status was irrelevant.

But no matter how much he told himself that going to the cove with Gracie was merely a walk with a friend, he wanted it to be more than that, and he hoped she did too. There was something about her that kept drawing him to her, and he'd never felt such a pull before.

He'd had girlfriends, of course he had, but none of them had touched him where it really mattered – his heart.

Giving himself a mental shake, he tackled the panini. He was being silly. He'd only known the woman for less than a fortnight, so she couldn't possibly have touched his heart, but he found his thoughts returning to her time and time again, and he wondered what it was about her that he found so appealing.

She was pretty, although she didn't appear to realise it, and introspective. She was creative in a quiet, thoughtful way, and her love of finding a use for old material gelled with his own conclusion that society was too wasteful for its own good. He hated the idea of all those old clothes being incinerated because they were made from synthetic material that couldn't easily be broken down into their component parts and reused. But at least the charity made a small amount from the contents of each bin, and when that was multiplied by all the UnderCover shops across the country, over the course of a year it added up to a considerable sum.

After a third cup of coffee and now buzzing from too much caffeine, Lucas waved goodbye to Eleri and was heading for home when an idea occurred to him.

There was a shop in Applewell called Pins to Elephants. It had been there since before he'd been born, and he hoped the family-run business would continue to do well for years

to come. It had caught his attention because of what it sold –
everything from pins to elephants as the saying went.

He'd bet his last penny that it sold coffee machines.

The thought of being able to have a proper cup of coffee
when he got up in the morning had him hurrying inside.

Good Lord, Tony was still running the place he saw, as he
spied the familiar if somewhat older face behind the counter.
Lucas used to love coming into Pins to Elephants when he was a
kid because they sold marbles, and automatically his eyes sought
out the shelf where they used to be kept.

The layout had changed over the years, of course, and the
shelf now contained a selection of coasters and placemats.

'Can I help?'

Lucas looked up to see Tony standing a few feet away.

'I was after a coffee machine, if you've got one,' he said.

'Do you want an automatic or a manual? Or we do combi
ones?'

Lucas thought he'd died and had gone to heaven. 'Can I have
a look?'

'Certainly. Would this be for your mum or yourself?'

'Er, both I suppose.' He had a perfectly good machine in
London, so it would make sense to leave the new one in
Applewell for his mother to use. In which case, she probably
wouldn't want an all-singing, all-dancing one, and something
simpler might be better. He couldn't envisage her grinding her
own beans, for instance.

'I'm only asking because she was in here earlier and she
bought one of these.' Tony led him down an aisle and stopped
when he came to an impressive selection of coffee machines.
He pointed one out; it wasn't cheap.

Lucas thought of the jar of instant in the cupboard above the
kettle, and he knew the machine wasn't for herself: *his mother
had bought it for him.*

His heart constricted at her thoughtfulness, and he felt like
crying. He didn't deserve a mother like her. If she'd turned him

away and told him never to darken her door again, it would have been no less than he deserved.

Thanking Tony and saying he'd better check with his mum first before he bought anything, Lucas went home. Sure enough, sitting on the kitchen table, complete with the length of pink ribbon she'd salvaged from the bouquet of flowers he'd given her, sat a brand-new coffee machine.

When he read the note accompanying it, tears slid down his cheeks.

'I love you, too, Mum,' he whispered. 'I love you, too...'

Chapter 16

Gracie

Gracie had never been one for lying in bed on Sunday mornings, probably because she rarely went anywhere on Saturday evenings so was usually in bed by eleven at the latest and sometimes earlier. Today was no exception, so after her breakfast she cleaned the kitchen, did a few more chores, then decided to make use of the time until Lucas called for her.

There was always something she could be going on with, and she normally had several projects on the go at once, moving from one to the other as the mood took her. This morning, with UnderCover on her mind, courtesy of Lucas, she decided to do her bit for the charity and mend the red coat. It would probably take her half an hour, possibly even less, which would be good because she could move on to a dress whose zip had stuck. If she could free it, she would, but if not, she'd replace it, and both items could be returned to UnderCover to be sold.

She also had a ball gown in her sights, one she'd had for a while, and she'd been waiting for inspiration to strike. It was rather old fashioned, very 1980s with huge puff sleeves, a sweetheart neckline and a full skirt, and she was fairly certain no one would wear it as it was. However, the fabric was lovely and there was so much of it that if she unpicked some of the seams she was certain she could make it into something far more modern.

The problem was, it would take her a good chunk of time, and time meant money, especially when she had no outlet to sell such a thing. She could always give it back to UnderCover, but the charity would probably only get £20 or less for it, and when Gracie thought of all the hours she'd have to put in, it would be more cost effective for her to cut the dress up and use the material to make things she could sell in her own shop.

The waste made her feel sad. Someone had loved that dress once. Someone had chosen it and worn it, and hopefully had a wonderful time in it.

Oh well… Gracie mused on it as she worked on the coat, and she was still thinking about it as she snipped the last thread from the red coat and inspected it. Perfect. No one would ever be able to tell it had been repaired.

She draped it around a dressmaker's mannequin so it didn't get creased, and turned her attention to the dress with the dodgy zip.

She was still trying to free it and was about to give up when there was a knock at the door and she realised the time.

Damn! Lucas was here and she wasn't ready. She'd had a shower and washed her hair this morning, but she'd intended to change out of the joggers she liked to wear around the house, and into a pair of jeans.

Feeling a little embarrassed, she opened the door and almost stopped breathing.

He looked gorgeous. The hint of stubble on his cheeks gave him a slightly rugged appearance, and he wore a pair of badly faded jeans, a black T-shirt with the name of an old heavy metal band emblazoned on the front, and had a leather biker jacket slung over his shoulders.

He looked good enough to eat, and Gracie found herself drooling.

It was rare for her to have such a visceral reaction to a guy, and it left her breathless and rattled.

'I, erm, need to get changed,' she said, glancing down at her scruffy joggers and equally scruffy top. That was the problem when she was immersed in her work – she lost track of time. 'Come in, I won't be a sec.'

She stood to the side to let him pass and caught a delicious whiff of his cologne, and she sniffed appreciatively. Boy, he smelt good. Her tummy turned over and she took a deep breath to steady herself, but it only made things worse because she got another noseful of his unique scent that sent her into a tailspin of nervousness.

'Would you like a tea or a coffee?' she asked.

'It depends on how long you intend to be,' he countered with a slow smile which did nothing for her nerves.

'A minute or two,' she said, pointing in the direction of the living room door. She noticed his curious gaze as he walked past her front room. The door was open, and he glanced inside and she saw him hesitate; she wished she'd had the presence of mind to close it, because the room wasn't the tidiest. How could it be when it was full of all the things she was working on? It was as tidy as she could keep it, but to anyone who had been expecting to see a sofa and a TV, or a dining table, it was bound to be a shock.

'In here,' she said, showing him into her tiny living room. The house she lived in was over a hundred years old and had originally been one of a row of farm worker cottages. Terraced and small, it still had the three separate downstairs rooms, consisting of a kitchen, a living room, and what would have been the parlour in days gone by, which would have been kept for best and only used when the vicar came to visit. That room was now her workroom and, unlike many homeowners in the same street, she hadn't turned the two rooms into one to make a larger space. The original layout suited her needs perfectly. With only herself living there, she didn't need a bigger sitting room.

But what she did need was to get a move on and change into something more suitable for going to the cove.

She left Lucas standing awkwardly in the centre of the living room as she dashed upstairs, and when she took off her clothes and rooted around for a lightweight top, she was very conscious of him being below her feet while she was half-naked, and the awareness raised goosebumps on the skin of her arms.

Muttering that she needed to pull herself together, she hurriedly dragged on some clothes, ran her fingers through her hair (brushing it would only make it frizzier than it already was), then hunted for her trainers. She took a quick look in the mirror, noticing she had more colour in her cheeks than usual, and darted back downstairs.

Lucas wasn't where she'd left him; he was in the hall and for the second time in less than ten minutes she wished she'd closed the door to her workroom. However, she had no intention of apologising for the state of it. What she did in her own house was her own affair, and he knew she had a business to run. Besides, he'd seen for himself that the living room was tidy and— She was overthinking it, wasn't she? He was probably in the hall because he couldn't wait to get going. Or maybe because he felt uncomfortable being in her house. His frown was probably due to the fact that she was keeping him waiting.

'Sorry about that,' she said, almost falling down the last three steps in her haste to reach the bottom.

Lucas's hands shot out and he caught her arms to steady her.

Gracie froze at the unexpected contact, her eyes widening.

He swiftly released her, and she giggled nervously. 'Oops,' she said. 'Thanks. Clumsy me. I don't normally fall down my own stairs.'

'Glad to hear it.' He was looking at her strangely.

'Shall we get going?' she asked, gesturing for him to go ahead of her. Her arms tingled where he'd gripped her and she felt like rubbing them, but she didn't want him to think he'd hurt her. Not when the opposite was true.

She locked the door, dropped the keys in her pocket, and they set off.

It was strange walking beside him. It would have felt strange walking beside any man who wasn't her dad, and she didn't quite know what to say or how to behave. Occasionally their arms bumped, and she had to force herself not to flinch as though she'd been scalded. She was acutely conscious of him: his height, the length of his stride, the sheer male magnetism of him.

Gracie scoffed silently at her fanciful imaginings. Male magnetism, indeed. She'd be comparing him to a rock star or a film icon next. Her attraction to him was undeniable, but he was just an ordinary guy. He wasn't charismatic or anything. Just good-looking. And friendly. And here, with her. Which was significant in itself, considering the lack of male attention she usually experienced.

It was her own fault, really. She wasn't vivacious, or even mildly outgoing. Unless she was discussing fabric or sewing, she tended to be tongue-tied and awkward. And, let's be honest, despite the move towards gender equality, on the west coast of Wales in a rural place like Applewell it was women who were more interested in sewing and dressmaking, and even then it was a dying art. This was proved by the sheer volume of garments that were donated to charity. Years ago nothing would have been wasted, and things would have been mended. Now, though, they were simply discarded. Or, if the item of clothing was valuable enough (and Gracie didn't necessarily mean in monetary terms) it was brought to her for mending. In her great-grandma's day, the mending would have taken place at home.

'Have you ever seen a darning mushroom?' she asked suddenly, wondering how many people would even know what one was.

'A what now?'

Gracie blushed. For a second, she'd been so engrossed in her thoughts she'd forgotten it was Lucas by her side, and she'd spoken to him as though he was Catrin.

'A darning mushroom,' she muttered.

'Is it edible?'

Gracie giggled, then blushed harder. 'Only if you're a wood-worm.'

'You've lost me.' He was gazing down at her with an amused expression on his face, but he wasn't laughing at her. His smile was soft, indulgent almost.

'It's a piece of wood that looks like a mushroom and is used for darning things. I remember my great-grandma darning socks with one. They were woollen ones, not the three pairs for five quid from the supermarket. Fair Isle socks, they were, and I think she might have knitted them herself. Whenever they got a hole in the toe, or the heel started to wear through, she used to darn them.'

'I never knew you could darn socks.'

'I don't expect you wanted to know, either,' Gracie said, quietly. Unless you were a crafter, things like darning didn't usually hold great appeal. Why on earth had she asked him such a ridiculous question?

'One of my granny's friends used to knit a lot,' he said. 'I remember she made all Nora's bonnets and booties, and teeny-tiny cardigans.'

'Would that be Alys Griffiths? She used to live on Oak Lane in the house next door to your sister. It was she who taught me to knit. And she taught me how to crochet, and do something called tatting.'

'What is that?'

They'd walked through the village and out the other side and were just about to turn down onto an overgrown path. It led to a small, narrow, steep-sided valley, heavily wooded and with a stream trickling through it. Unless you knew the path was there, you wouldn't see it as it was very well hidden, and the residents of Applewell were keen to keep it that way because at the far end of the valley was a small cove with a secluded beach, sheltered by those very cliffs on which she'd eaten her fish and chip supper last Saturday. Tourists didn't often go there, and that was the way the villagers wanted it to stay.

The path was rather steep and could be dicey if it had been raining, and when Lucas said, 'I'll go first in case you slip,' Gracie didn't argue. If she was truthful, the idea of skidding and having him break her fall was an appealing one.

They were halfway down the path before Lucas reminded her that he'd asked about tatting.

'It's a form of lace-making, using little shuttles and all done by hand,' she told him. 'The thread often tends to be thicker than that of the lace you'd find on, say, a wedding dress. Think doilies. They used to be popular years and years ago for putting things like vases or bowls on, to protect your wooden furniture.'

'I vaguely remember seeing something like that.' He glanced back at her. 'You can make those?'

'Anyone can make them. You could, if you want,' she joked. 'I could teach you.'

'I might take you up on that.'

Was he flirting with her? It happened so rarely that she couldn't tell.

Without warning, Gracie's foot, the one she had most of her weight on, skidded out from underneath her and she let out a squeal.

Lucas's hand shot out. He caught her around the waist and stopped her from ending up on her bottom, pulling her hard against him.

He staggered slightly but both his balance and his grip held, and she found herself pressed up against his chest, her face inches from his.

'Are you OK?' He was staring down at her, concern etched across his features.

'I'm fine, honestly.' She cleared her throat and gently pulled back from him, her pulse hammering. 'You must think I'm a total klutz.'

'Not at all,' he replied gallantly.

Gracie was blushing again, and she cursed her wayward cheeks. His swift response had saved her from a muddy backside, that was all. She'd slipped and stumbled on this path more times than she'd had hot dinners over the years, and had never done herself any greater harm than having a dirty behind, grimy hands, and the odd scrape. This was no big deal. Really, it wasn't.

'Thank you,' she said, belatedly.

'You're welcome.' He turned around and proceeded down the path again, and she breathed a sigh of relief.

It was only a minute or so later that the valley floor began to level out and tantalising glimpses of the beach and the sea became visible through the trees. The air smelt less of woodland, fresh water and ferns, and more of salt and seaweed. She breathed deeply, filling her lungs with fresh briny air, trying to drive out Lucas's delicious scent which still lingered in her nose.

As one, they paused when their feet hit the line of pebbles and driftwood which indicated the high tide mark, and stopped to take in the view.

'God, how I've missed this,' Lucas said, his chest heaving as he drew breath after breath of sea air into his lungs. His face was lifted towards the sun and his eyes scanned the horizon.

Gracie followed suit, tilting her face skywards and feeling warmth on her cheeks that, for once, had nothing to do with embarrassment. The sound of waves breaking as the tide retreated, the gentle gurgle of the stream as it reached the sand, carving an ever-changing route to the sea, and the cries of the swooping gulls high on the cliffs, was the music of her childhood.

Suddenly he was off, racing down the sand, kicking off his trainers as he went, hopping as he tried to tear off his socks. 'Last one in is a scaredy cat,' he yelled over his shoulder as he ran towards the water. He didn't stop until he reached the waves, and even then it was only to roll up the hem of his cut-off jeans so the fabric was over his knees.

Gracie watched him in amazement, then she too was careening down the sand, her own trainers discarded. Sockless, she reached the water's edge, feeling the suck of the wavelets as they retreated and regrouped for another watery assault.

She rolled up her jeans as far as they would go, then she was ankle deep in the small waves, the golden sand caressing her toes, and the chill of the water made her squeal and laugh. Suddenly she was having more fun than she'd had in years, and she had Lucas Grainger to thank.

Who'd have thought it!

Chapter 17

Lucas

Lucas's sudden urge to race headlong down the beach had taken him by surprise almost as much as it had shocked Gracie. He'd left her standing as he took off, kicking his feet free of his trainers and hopping momentarily when it came to yanking his socks off. He'd thrown each item away with joyful abandon, feeling like a kid again, not caring if they landed on wet sand and got soaked.

As he ran, his feet had slapped against the compacted sand, sending up splashes of water, and the wind was in his face, and he felt freer than he'd done for more years than he could remember. Laughing out loud, he'd reached the water's edge and the creeping wavelets, and he'd stopped to roll his cut-off jeans up over his knees. Then he was in the sea, the chilly water lapping around his ankles, his toes sinking into the sand, and he'd waded deeper until the water reached mid-calf and the waves were higher.

He'd been aware of Gracie following him into the sea, her progress slower – but then, he'd had the advantage of surprise. Her squeal as her feet were enveloped by cold water made him smile wider than he was already, and when her laughter rang out, he joined in.

Gracie's face was glowing, her eyes sparkling and full of mischief as she kicked water at him, then danced away as the droplets fell on him. The bottom of his jeans were getting wet but what did he care? He bent down to scoop handfuls of water, sending her running and shrieking out of the sea and dashing up the beach. But a moment later, she was back kicking again, and spray flew up into the air, the droplets catching the sun as they fell, until they were both sodden, Gracie more than Lucas as she'd been unable to roll her skinny jeans up as far as he had.

Eventually, she'd had enough and she retreated, shaking her head and laughing, trying to ease the wet material away from her legs without success. His gaze followed, travelling down the length of her body, and he realised how petite she was, how tall he felt in comparison, and he wanted to scoop her up.

But of course, he didn't. Instead, he followed her up the beach, admiring the view of her as much as he'd admired the view of the cove, watching as she bent to retrieve discarded items of footwear.

'I believe this is yours,' she said, picking up a soggy sock with a thumb and forefinger and holding it out to him.

He took it, equally disgusted. Not only was it wet, but it was covered in sand. Her socks had fared no better and, as he and Gracie retreated up the beach, they gravitated towards the stream and rinsed their socks in the fresh water.

Lucas helicoptered his around his head after wringing out as much moisture as he could but was finally forced to admit defeat; they weren't going to dry any time soon.

'Do you have to rush back?' he asked. When she shook her head, he found a smooth rock to sit on and he spread his socks out to dry.

She gave him a disdainful look. 'I mightn't have to rush off,' she said, 'but I'd like to go home before it gets dark. You do realise they're not going to be dry for hours?'

'Don't care,' he said, sounding remarkably like an eleven-year-old version of himself. 'How long do you think before they'll be dry enough to put on?'

'Several hours.' She paused. 'When you're in London, who does your washing?'

'Me,' he replied, wondering why she wanted to know, then he realised what she was getting at. 'I live in a flat with no outside space. I've got a tumble dryer.' He knew how long to set the dryer for and at what temperature, but he had no clue how long it would take to air-dry a sock.

She shook her head sadly. 'You've got a lot to learn.'

'I don't feel my education has been lacking because I don't know the air-drying time of a pair of socks,' he replied loftily.

'Your mother would beg to differ. She always says that the only thing that beats the smell of bread baking is the smell of washing that has been dried outdoors. Is it strange being back?'

'A bit,' he conceded. Actually, more than a bit, but as the days rolled by, he felt himself slotting back into village life, the strangeness of being in Applewell eroded by familiarity. He'd expected to find it boring after the initial excitement and discomfort, but instead he found it comforting, and he could feel echoes of the seventeen-year-old youth he'd once been shake his head in despair at all those lost years in between. He might have run away physically, but he'd not taken his soul with him. The longer he spent in Applewell, the more the fragmented pieces of himself bonded together. He wasn't whole yet – far from it – but he now had hopes that one day he might be.

'I think I'm beginning to settle in now, though,' he added. 'It helps that I've been keeping myself busy.' He ignored Gracie's curious look. The real reason he was in Applewell was no one else's business.

'I understand you've been working in UnderCover most days.'

'I have! It's been fun.' He was surprised to hear himself say that, but it was true. 'I enjoy chatting to customers, even if many of the locals who come into the shop do so out of curiosity about me. It seemed, for the first few days at least, that I was still something of a sensation.' He tilted his head back, letting the sun bathe his face in warmth, and closed his eyes. 'I'm surprised the villagers were so interested. I expect you heard that my mum put a banner out?'

Gracie laughed softly. 'I heard. It's not you who everyone is interested in now, though. It's Catrin's welfare. They are popping in to make sure she's all right.'

'Ah, I see.' That made sense. She had been, and still was, upset about her breakup with her partner.

Thinking about Catrin reminded him of what he'd seen in Gracie's house. He'd spotted the red coat the moment he'd glanced into what would have originally been the "best room" in the house, but now appeared to be a work room of sorts. It had been draped over a tailor's dummy and had looked suspiciously like the one with the torn shoulder seam that he'd put in UnderCover's waste material bin on Monday.

But what had really alerted him was the nervous look on Gracie's face when she saw him glance through the open door and spot it. It was quite fortuitous that she'd then gone upstairs to change, leaving him alone for a few minutes, and he'd snatched the opportunity to nip into her work space and take a closer look.

Careful not to disturb anything, he'd examined the coat as thoroughly as he could, especially the area around the seam where the arm was attached to the shoulder, and it was only because he was looking for it that he was able to see the expert repair. If he hadn't already known there had been damage in that area, he never would have been able to tell.

He had to say that for Gracie, she was a darned good seamstress.

The question that had been, and still was, in the forefront of Lucas's mind, was what did she intend to do with the coat now? The only reason for her to repair it that he could think of was to sell it. He'd been pondering what her arrangement was with Catrin (did they split the profits? Did Catrin get a percentage?) when Gracie came back down the stairs, saw him, and had almost fallen down them.

He'd wondered if this second bout of nerves had been because she guessed he'd been rooting around in her front room.

He supposed he should have asked her outright, caught her on the hop so to speak, but he wanted to know exactly what was going on before he said anything, because it was Catrin who would be the most affected if what he suspected was true. Stealing from one's employer was bad enough; stealing from the homeless was abhorrent and inexcusable. Waste textiles and garments might only be worth pennies, but as he'd thought before, the pennies soon added up. If the only thing he achieved in coming back to Applewell (aside from an improvement in his mental health) was rooting out a dishonest employee, then he'd consider his visit a success. Not that the residents of Applewell would see it that way...

The other question that had been playing on his mind since his discovery was how culpable Gracie might be. Was she in cahoots with Catrin, or was she under the impression that items not fit to be sold would end up in landfill? He hoped it was the latter, because if not it would affect how he felt about her.

'Catrin's a really lovely person,' Gracie said, breaking into his thoughts, and for one awful moment he worried that she had read his mind or that he'd said something out loud.

'She's a good saleswoman,' he replied noncommittally.

How *did* he feel about Gracie? He wasn't sure. Protective, maybe? That had been his first instinct at seeing her so upset when he'd met her on Oak Lane last weekend. Fascination was another emotion she provoked in him, and he was certainly attracted to her physically. Her ethics regarding trying to do her bit for the planet were also appealing.

'Have you decided when you're going back to London?' Gracie asked, feeling her own socks for signs of drying, before grimacing and turning them over.

He brushed the dried sand off his feet and wiggled his toes. 'Not yet.' The hustle and sheer busyness of the city filled him with momentary dread. The thought of returning to a life of sucking up to people to try to weasel a few measly pounds out of them (actually, many of the amounts were quite substantial sums of money) made him go cold. He might be of far more use to UnderCover doing what he was paid to do, but he'd felt more fulfilled by working in the shop this week than he had done for many, many months by doing his actual job.

'I don't think these are going to dry any time soon,' he said, picking up his own socks and pulling a face. He ignored Gracie's told-you-so expression. 'Fancy a coffee on the way back?' He saw her hesitation, and added, 'My treat.'

'I was actually going to pop into The Busy Bumble,' she said. 'They do a mean Sunday lunch.'

'So does my mum. Would you care to join us?' Now where had that come from, he wondered. One second he was suggesting a quick coffee and the next he'd invited her for Sunday lunch.

'Oh, I don't think so. I wouldn't want to put Vivien out.'

'You won't be putting her out. She'd love to have you join us.' Lucas, if he was honest, had no idea whether his mother would be pleased or not, but there would certainly be enough food to go round if last Sunday's roast dinner was anything to go by. There had been so much of it that Lucas had expected Nora, Ianto and Ruby to show up. He'd eaten far more than he'd intended because he hated to see food go to waste, and had ended up going on a ten-mile run later that evening in order to burn the extra calories he'd consumed.

'You'd be doing me a favour,' he said. 'You ought to see the amount of food she cooked last week. I know I'm a big guy, but it seems my mother is intent on making me even bigger.'

'I like big men,' Gracie said, then clapped a hand to her mouth. Her face, already glowing from the sun, coloured further. 'I didn't mean it like that. You're not *big*, big. You're tall. And well-built. Ooh, I didn't mean that, either. What I meant was, you're muscley with wide shoulders.' She groaned. 'I'll stop talking now.'

'Please don't,' he said, amused. Her embarrassment was endearing. She was cute when she blushed. She was cute, full stop. 'So...' He swivelled around on the rock to face her. 'You like big men, do you?' Then he ducked as she threw a wet sock at him.

Laughing, he slipped his feet into his trainers, feeling the grit of stubborn sand between his toes, and stood up.

'Don't you think you should check with your mum, first?' Gracie asked.

'Does that mean you'll come to lunch?'

'I'm going to have to – I want to see just how much you can eat in one sitting.' She glanced at him from under her lashes as she wriggled her feet into her own trainers, and he felt a flutter in his stomach that had nothing to do with hunger.

When he held out his hand to help her to her feet, the touch of her skin on his made his pulse race.

Blimmin' heck, what was going on?

Never had he experienced such a reaction to a woman. And he had no clue how to deal with it.

Chapter 18

Gracie

Gracie liked Vivien, but they weren't exactly close and she wasn't sure how the woman would feel about having Gracie descend on her unannounced, and for lunch no less, so it was with a certain amount of trepidation that she walked to Lucas's house.

What on earth had possessed her to agree?

The only excuse she could find was that she'd felt so flustered and embarrassed after telling him she liked big men (really, she'd actually *said* that?) that she'd have accepted an invitation from the devil himself.

That she liked being with Lucas and didn't want the morning to end had nothing whatsoever to do with anything.

Except it did, she was forced to acknowledge as they strolled through the streets of Applewell, garnering a few curious glances. Gracie smiled politely at people but didn't say anything, and she knew the gossip mill would be busy grinding out rumours by the afternoon.

Liking Lucas was daft. For one thing he was only visiting Applewell, and although she didn't know how long he was going to be here for, he'd eventually leave at some point. Secondly, he was way out of her league. Quirky was possibly the kindest description for herself. Wild, untamed hair (aka frizzy), slightly staring eyes, too-wide mouth, freckles... She might have got away with being a plain Jane, if it wasn't for the fact that her personality was as plain as her looks. Therefore, she surmised, Lucas was simply being friendly and any attraction she felt (and she felt it in spades) was one-sided and doomed.

Which begged the question: why was she putting herself through this? What purpose would it serve, apart from making her feel even lonelier than she already felt?

The aroma of roast beef assailed her nose the moment Lucas opened the front door and shepherded her inside his mum's house. Gracie sniffed the air hungrily. Oh well, at least she'd get a proper homecooked meal out of this, if nothing else.

'Mum, I've brought someone back with me,' he called, stepping around her and heading down the short hall to the single door. To the left of it was a staircase.

Gracie glanced around curiously. Vivien lived in the same-sized terraced cottage as the one she lived in, but unlike Gracie, Vivien had knocked the two small reception rooms into one and had blocked up the door to the former front room. The living room, Gracie noticed when she walked hesitantly into it, was bright and airy, with light flooding in from windows at either end. Leading off from the living room was the kitchen and she knew without being told that there would be a loo beyond that. She also guessed that the bathroom would be directly above the kitchen and that there were two, possibly three bedrooms if the original larger front bedroom had been split into two.

Vivien appeared in the kitchen doorway, a tea towel in her hand. She was wearing an apron and a smile, the latter widening when she saw Gracie.

'Gracie, how lovely to see you,' she said, coming towards her. 'You must excuse me, I'm in the middle of cooking lunch. I was just about to serve up, actually.'

Gracie heard the unspoken message – whatever you're here for, make it quick because we'll be sitting down to eat in a minute.

'I've invited her to lunch,' Lucas said. 'I hope you don't mind? Last week you cooked enough to feed the street.'

Gracie studied Vivien's expression as the older woman processed the news, and she saw a slight hesitation and a brief frown flit across Vivien's face before she declared, 'Of course I don't mind. It's nice you brought a friend home.'

'I'm not twelve, Mum,' he said, shaking his head and smiling. 'You'll be telling me to go out to play until it's ready, next.'

'No, I won't,' was Vivien's swift retort. 'I'll be telling you to wash your hands and lay the table.'

'That put me in my place,' Lucas said to Gracie. 'Take a seat.' He nodded towards the sofa and followed his mum into the kitchen.

'Is there anything I can do?' Gracie called. She didn't want to sit down and make herself at home; she felt awkward and uncertain, and she was sure her presence was an imposition.

'Nah, Mum's got it under control,' he called out.

Nervously, she turned around slowly, examining the room. At the end nearest the kitchen was a dining table and six chairs, and a sideboard rested up against where the chimney breast would have been. That was another difference between her house and Vivien's – Vivien had removed both fireplaces and the associated chimney breasts, which had opened up the space. Gracie still had the alcoves on either side of hers, that contained the original inbuilt cupboards.

When she saw how much more space Vivien had, she was envious; but she also loved the original features her own little house retained, and she smiled to herself, thinking that if anyone had been asked to guess which woman lived in which house, they would have been forgiven for assuming that the older woman lived in the least modern house.

She broke off her musing when Lucas reappeared with a handful of cutlery and some placemats.

'It'll be about ten minutes, Mum said, so if you want to wash your hands and freshen up, the bathroom is upstairs,' he told her, laying out the knives and forks.

Gracie, keen to escape if only for a few minutes, headed up the stairs, located the bathroom, and slipped inside, closing the door behind her and letting out a sigh of relief. Once again, she wondered what had possessed her to agree to have lunch with him, and in his mum's house at that. Being in the cafe with him would have been stressful enough, but this was excruciating, and they hadn't even sat down to eat yet.

However, after washing her hands and face and running damp fingers through her impossible hair, she felt a little calmer and was able to plaster a friendly smile on her lips and go back downstairs.

A couple of tureens of vegetables sat in the middle of the table, along with a plate sporting thinly carved slices of beef, crispy golden roast potatoes and fluffy Yorkshire puddings.

Gracie's stomach rumbled and her mouth watered. This was a real treat and suddenly she was glad she'd accepted Lucas's invitation. The conversation might be stilted and she might feel incredibly embarrassed, but she was certain that the amazing lunch she was about to eat would more than make up for any discomfort. Gracie hated cooking, and the nearest she got to meal creation was to open a can of soup or throw two pieces of bread on a plate and slap something in the middle of them.

This looked lovely, and her appreciation must have shown in her face because as Vivien came in carrying yet another tureen in oven-gloved hands, Lucas following behind with the plates, Vivien smiled warmly at her.

'Sit down and get stuck in,' Vivien instructed.

Gracie, conscious that the bottoms of her jeans were still wet, gingerly took a seat, hoping she was sitting in the correct place and wondering if maybe she was overthinking things.

Lucas sat opposite her and began to ladle roasties onto his plate. Gracie put her hands in her lap and watched him.

'Don't be shy,' he said. 'Here.' He scooped up a potato and dumped it on her plate, then spooned up another.

'Here's the gravy,' his mother said, putting a large ceramic jug in the centre of the table. 'Gracie, I hope you're going to have more than that,' she cried, eyeing Gracie's almost empty plate.

'She's being shy,' Lucas repeated.

Gracie thought that if he only knew just how shy she actually was, he wouldn't tease her. Vivien, however, did know; it was no secret, and without saying anything further she picked up Gracie's plate and piled it high with meat and vegetables before making a grab for the gravy before Lucas got his hands on it. 'Say when,' she instructed, starting to pour.

'When,' Gracie said, and accepted the laden plate with a smile of thanks.

'Lucas mentioned that you went to the beach this morning,' Vivien said, serving herself. Lucas had already waded into his meal and was chewing enthusiastically, although judging by the food still in the tureens, he had a fair way to go if he wanted to make any inroads into the amount Vivien had cooked. Gracie realised Lucas hadn't been exaggerating.

A fork halfway to her lips, Gracie said, 'He suggested a walk to the cove because he hadn't been there in years.' She popped the portion of gravy-covered Yorkshire pudding into her mouth and closed her eyes in bliss. My word, the gravy was to die for!

'It hasn't changed a bit,' Lucas said. 'It's as unspoilt as ever.' He eyed the mound of carrots as his fork hovered over it, and took a deep breath before diving in.

'He said you went for a paddle.' Vivien had a far more modest amount of food on her plate.

'This is absolutely delicious,' Gracie said. 'I'd say I'm sorry to intrude, but after tasting your gravy I'd be lying. Yes, we paddled and the water was freezing.' She astonished herself at being able to speak so naturally, even going as far as to joke about her unexpected arrival.

'I didn't make the gravy – Lucas did. He's not a bad cook when he puts his mind to it.' Vivien sent her son an indulgent smile.

Gracie's eyebrows shot up. '*You* made the gravy?'

'Is that so odd?' he asked, grinning.

'Not at all, although you put me to shame. I can't boil an egg.'

'I bet you can.'

'She can't,' Vivien confirmed. 'Which is why she eats in Eleri's cafe most days.'

'Well, then, I'll have to cook a meal or two for you,' Lucas said, and Gracie reddened.

'I wasn't hinting—' she began.

'I know you weren't, but I like cooking. I find it soothing and it's a complete change from staring at a computer all day or being in meetings. I like creating new dishes.' He paused. 'I suppose you do your creating in other ways.'

'She's very clever with a needle, and I don't know where she gets all her wonderful ideas from,' Vivien said. 'Have some more peas.'

'Um… I haven't finished the ones I've got,' Gracie protested.

Vivien ignored her and popped another spoonful on her plate.

Gracie wondered how she was going to manage to eat it all. 'I might have to come for a run with you later,' she said to Lucas.

'You'd be more than welcome.' He grinned at her, and she grinned back, enjoying their joke.

'I didn't know you were a runner,' Vivien said.

'I'm not, but if you keep putting any more food on my plate, I think I'll have to be.'

'Give over! There's hardly anything of you. You're a little scrap of a thing.'

'You're comparing her to me and Nora,' Lucas said. 'I'm six-two and our Nora's five-foot-nine.'

'How tall are you, Gracie?' Vivien asked, and Gracie's face flooded with colour. She could cope with the odd bit of banter, but being the centre of attention was beyond her.

'Er, five-foot-three.'

'She's tiny, isn't she, Lucas?'

'She's perfect.' Lucas froze and his eyes widened, and Gracie was fairly certain he'd not meant it to come out the way it sounded.

Vivien stared at him, her gaze full of speculation.

'She wouldn't look right if she was six inches taller,' he amended. 'Just as Nora would look odd shorter.'

'I don't know where the two of you get your height from,' Vivien said, and the awkwardness melted away as Lucas joked that it was due to all the hearty meals she'd put in front of them.

'She used to force us to eat our vegetables first,' he complained. 'I still don't like sprouts, but she'd never listen.'

'I haven't cooked sprouts today,' his mother pointed out.

'Thank God!' Lucas's reply was heartfelt.

'I quite like sprouts,' Gracie said. She didn't mind talking about food; she might dislike the process of preparing and cooking it, but she certainly enjoyed eating it.

'A girl after my own heart,' Vivien said with feeling. 'Next time, I'll do us a couple of handfuls.'

Gracie looked stricken, praying that Vivien didn't think she'd just invited herself to lunch.

'We'll have a nice bit of roast lamb and mint sauce,' Vivien said. 'It'll be better than sitting in The Busy Bumble on your own. Eleri's cafe isn't open on Sundays,' she said to Lucas.

To be fair, Gracie didn't have to sit on her own if she didn't want to. There was always someone in the pub who she knew and who would probably be happy to have her sit with them. But she didn't like to intrude, so she normally took a book with her and buried her nose in it instead. And she didn't always go to the pub on Sundays: sometimes she ate beans on toast at home, or had a bowl of soup, or a Pot Noodle.

'Please don't—' She was about to say 'Please don't think I'm inviting myself' when Vivien leapt in.

'It's no bother. I'll be cooking for this great big oaf, so I can just as easy cook for three as for two.'

'Don't,' Lucas said, and Gracie's heart dropped. Lucas didn't want her here at all.

She felt the sting of tears and she cast her eyes down to her plate, not wanting either of them to see the hurt she felt.

'If you cook for three you may as well invite Nora, Ianto, Ruby and Mrs Henderson next door, because there'll be so much food,' he joked.

Gracie didn't know what to feel now, apart from silly.

'That's an idea. Gracie, you know our Nora, don't you? And Ianto's a lovely lad. It'll be no bother. Please say you'll come.' Vivien had a strangely pleading expression in her eyes.

Gracie glanced at Lucas. He was nodding.

'We could go for a walk again beforehand if you like,' he suggested. 'Maybe along the cliffs next time. If that's OK?'

'How about if the pair of you take Ruby to the beach?' his mum suggested. 'I don't think she's had a chance to play with the bucket and spade you bought her yet.'

'Good idea,' Lucas said. 'Do you think Nora would let me?'

Vivien gave it some thought. 'Probably not,' she conceded. 'Ruby doesn't know you.' She sent him an apologetic look.

Lucas nodded sadly. 'I know.'

'How about if Nora and Ianto go with you?' Gracie suggested.

He thought for a moment as he chewed. 'I'll ask her, but I'd still like you to come, Gracie. I can try to get to know Ruby while you keep Nora occupied.'

'OK, if your sister is happy with that.'

'Even if she isn't and she doesn't want to go to the beach, there's nothing preventing the two of you from going for a walk, then coming for lunch afterwards.' Vivien was giving her that look again, and Gracie hesitated before replying, as she tried to work out the meaning behind it.

Then she got it, and her heart went out to the woman; Vivien wanted Gracie there to act as a buffer between Lucas and his sister. Gracie had heard that Nora hadn't welcomed Lucas with open arms, unlike their mother, and that she still harboured resentment towards him for the hurt he'd caused. Gracie could understand that, but he seemed anxious to make amends.

If her presence would make the situation any easier on Sunday, then of course Gracie would come to lunch.

'If you're sure,' she said, some hesitancy still remaining.

'I'm sure,' Vivien replied, firmly.

There was one thing Gracie *was* sure about – that Lucas would be in Applewell for another week at least – and she discovered she was ridiculously pleased about it.

–

'Let me help,' Gracie said, getting to her feet and reaching for Lucas's empty plate. Hats off to him, he'd managed to put away a pretty substantial lunch, as had she.

Lucas snatched it away. 'Oh, no, you don't. I'll wash up – you relax with Mum.'

Gracie hovered for a moment, saw he was resolute, then sank back into her seat.

Would it be rude to eat and run? she wondered. Without helping to clear up, she had nothing to do with her hands, and she felt surplus to requirements and slightly jittery.

She smiled uncertainly at Vivien as the pair of them watched Lucas collect the plates and tureens, shuttling them back and forth to the kitchen, the only noise being the clatter of cutlery and the clink of porcelain.

Eventually though, Gracie and Vivien were alone, and the sounds of water running in the sink and of saucepans being moved around were accompanied by a tuneless whistling from Lucas.

Gracie winced.

'He always used to do that when he was nervous,' Vivien said. 'It used to drive me to distraction.' Her expression was soft, and Gracie surmised that the woman didn't care what noise Lucas made now, as long as he was near enough for her to hear. 'I've been told he bought you flowers.' She glanced at her own bouquet sitting on the sideboard, which was past its best but still displaying lovely blooms.

'I hear he bought you flowers, too,' Gracie said. 'But then, you're his mum...' She sighed. 'He should have given them to Catrin – she deserves them more than I do.'

Gracie stared at her placemat. She could feel the weight of Vivien's gaze. It pinned her in place like a butterfly on a collector's board.

'Do you like my son?' Vivien asked. Idly she played with her dessert fork.

Gracie shrugged. 'I don't know,' she muttered. She knew what his mother meant.

'I think you do like him.'

'Even if I did, what would be the point? It's not like that. He's... I'm...'

'He likes you, too. I can tell.'

Gracie was tempted to say that Vivien didn't know her son as well as she hoped she did. He'd lived away from Applewell for years. He'd grown and changed, and Gracie would be very surprised if he bore much resemblance to the teenager who'd ran away all those years ago. His mother was trying to find remnants of the boy he had once been in the man he'd become, trying to establish a connection that time and distance had stretched and frayed.

'We're friends, that's all,' Gracie said, and even as the words left her lips, she wasn't sure how true they were. She hardly knew him, and vice versa. Even if they did have any kind of friendship, it was a new and tentative one.

'I'd like to see him settled,' Vivien said. The fork she was playing with spun around as she twirled it.

Gracie, hands in her lap, squirmed. 'Is there someone in London he's close to?' It wouldn't make any difference, because there was nothing between her and Lucas anyway, but she felt she had to ask. She wasn't sure whether Vivien was warning her off or not, and whether he had a special someone waiting for him in the city.

'No, I'm pretty certain there isn't.' She slapped a hand down on the fork to stop it spinning. 'I'd like him to settle here, in Applewell.'

'Is that likely to happen?' Gracie asked, her voice low, and she heard his mother's sigh.

'I doubt it. As much as I try to kid myself that Applewell is his home, his life is in London.'

'That's what I thought.' Gracie met Vivien's gaze, and Lucas's mother nodded in understanding.

'I wouldn't like to see you hurt,' Vivien said. 'You're a sweet girl.'

'Did someone mention sweet?' Lucas asked.

Gracie jumped as he stuck his head around the door.

'Who wants cheesecake?' he offered.

'We'll all have a slice,' Vivien said. Thankfully the mood was broken and the rest of the meal passed pleasantly enough until eventually Gracie was able to make her escape.

Or so she thought.

'I'll walk you home,' Lucas offered, as Gracie thanked Vivien for a lovely lunch and prepared to leave.

'No need, I can find my own way home,' Gracie joked feebly.

'I could do with a stroll.'

'Aren't you going out for a run later?' Gracie asked, biting her lip as she remembered how she'd teased him.

'Maybe this evening. You're welcome to join me.'

Gracie shuddered. She hadn't run anywhere since she was forced to do a mad dash across John Porter's field when a flock of sheep decided to chase her. She must have been about thirteen at the time. She'd managed to live the last decade and a half without doing anything more strenuous than a fast walk, and she didn't intend to start now.

'Sorry about my mum,' he said, once they were on the street and safely out of earshot. 'You don't have to come to lunch on Sunday. I don't want you to feel railroaded into it.'

Gracie was tempted to say she wouldn't come, but she thought of the look on Vivien's face, so what she said was, 'I don't mind, but only if you don't. She railroaded you into it, too. I mean, you might have other plans.'

'Nope, no other plans,' he said.

'It's a bit of a cheek.'

'What? My mother asking you to lunch?' He chuckled.

'My accepting her invitation without checking with you first.' They turned into Gracie's street and she steadfastly looked straight ahead not wanting to see his expression.

'If I hadn't been happy with you coming, I'd have said.'

'But we hardly know each other.'

'Is that a problem? How are we supposed to get to know each other if we don't spend any time together? I want to get to know you, Gracie; if you'll let me.'

She halted outside her house and hung her head, letting her hair obscure her face. She was tempted to ask him why he wanted to get to know her, but she thought she already knew the answer – he didn't have any friends in Applewell, Nora was still upset with him, and Catrin was kind of his employee. Gracie appeared to be his sole source of companionship.

Friends, that's what they were, and Gracie didn't have many of those herself, so she was grateful for another one in her life.

Why, though, did she feel so disappointed? Bereft, even. It wasn't as though he'd shown any interest in her in *that* way. And nor would he. A man like him could have any woman he wanted.

She'd have to make do with his friendship and try not to get too attached to him.

Gracie had no intention of having her heart broken. She'd managed to get to twenty-eight without falling in love; all she needed to do was to hold her emotions in check for a while longer and she'd come out of the other side of his fleeting visit to Applewell unscathed.

She'd enjoy his company – and his mum's cooking – and that would be the extent of it.

But if that was the case, why did the thought of Lucas leaving Applewell make her feel so miserable?

Chapter 19

Lucas

'Did she get home all right?' Lucas's mother wanted to know when he returned from walking Gracie home. She was in the kitchen, and he would bet his right arm that she was checking the standard of his washing up.

'She only lives a couple of streets away, Mum, and it's a Sunday afternoon. Of course she got home all right.'

'If that's the case, why did you feel the need to take her home?'

'I fancied stretching my legs.'

'That's not all you fancy,' was Vivien's swift reply.

'I don't know what you mean.' Lucas stuck his nose in the air.

'I'd like to see you settle down, Luc.'

'Eh?' Where did that come from?

His mother sighed as she hung a damp cloth over the edge of the sink to dry. 'You couldn't take your eyes off Gracie, but please don't love her and leave her. She doesn't deserve that.'

'Hang on; one minute you're saying you want me to settle down, the next you're saying you think I'll take up with Gracie then dump her.' Lucas was totally confused.

'What I'm saying is, if you're looking for a holiday romance, take your eyes off Gracie. If you're looking for something more, I'll be delighted. But we both know you won't be around long enough for that. You'll be going back to London.'

Lucas got a glass out of the cupboard and filled it from the tap, then he took a long drink of water to buy himself some time to respond. His mother had said a lot that needed unpicking and he wasn't sure where to start.

Finally, he said, 'I'm not looking for a relationship, casual or otherwise, and I don't want to settle down. As for not taking my eyes off Gracie... she's just a friend.'

'I'm not sure she thinks of you as just a friend.'

'Why do you say that?' There was nothing in the way she'd acted that made him believe she thought of him in any other way. There'd been no flirting and no coming-on to him, and she'd even been reluctant to have lunch with him next Sunday. If she fancied him, she had an odd way of showing it.

His mother walked past and went into the living room, saying, 'Don't trifle with her, that's all I ask. She's not worldly wise and I wouldn't like to see her hurt.'

Neither would Lucas. The thought of Gracie being hurt by anyone made him angry. Is that what had happened last Saturday when he'd met her on Oak Lane? Had someone hurt her? She'd told him she didn't have a boyfriend, but was the lack of a man in her life a recent thing?

'I'm going for a run,' he declared suddenly.

'You've only just come in.'

'That was a stroll. I need to clear my head.'

His mother gave him a knowing look and he turned away in confusion. Was she seeing something he wasn't?

Shorts and vest on, his feet encased in his running shoes, Lucas headed up Oak Lane and across the fields towards the coastal path. It would make a nice change from pounding tarmac, and the steep gradients along the cliffs as they dropped down to natural inlets and coves and back up again would give him far more of a workout than the relatively flat streets of his usual London route.

Half an hour later he was sweating, breath steady and heart rate elevated (but not too much), and his mind had gained a lucidity that only intense physical exercise gave him.

He saw things more clearly now, and the insight unsettled him. He liked Gracie – that was a given, why else would he seek her out? – however, the liking went deeper.

The path led steeply downwards and he adjusted his pace accordingly, taking shorter steps as he leant back slightly to account for gravity. The jar on his knees and ankles as his feet struck the ground made him grimace, but he knew that going up the other side of the cove would be ten times more painful.

He could see Gracie in his mind's eye, running down the beach after him, trainers and socks flying, her hair snapping behind her like a flag, the sun on her face. With her wild russet hair and creamy freckled skin, she was an autumn child, a creature of forest and dappled shade, and when he'd seen her racing down the beach, she'd looked as though she'd escaped from her woodland home to experience a sunny watery one, and once she'd had her fill she'd melt back into the trees and hide herself amongst them.

'Ow!' Lucas almost fell as his foot came down awkwardly on a rock and slipped off. He lost his balance for a second and staggered, throwing himself backwards rather than risk falling forwards and tumbling down the path, because if he did, he'd keep tumbling until he reached the rocks at the bottom where he'd probably do himself some serious damage.

Lucas sat for a moment amongst the tussocks of springy grass, his heart thumping and his breath coming in short gasps.

Blimey, that was a close call. He should have been concentrating on where he was going instead of daydreaming.

What a daydream, though. He didn't think he was a fanciful sort of person, so for him to imagine Gracie as a kind of wood nymph or sprite was sheer nonsense. She was arresting, though. Not classically beautiful, nor cosmetically enhanced perfection, and not even traditionally pretty. Gracie's beauty was something he was having trouble qualifying. He didn't seem able to find the words, but he suspected it would travel with her down the years and not be left behind along with her youth.

He wasn't just drawn to her looks, though. She was sassy in a back-seat kind of way: in total contrast to Nora, who was fiery and outspoken. He sensed a quiet strength, underneath the vulnerability.

Gracie might be unassuming and a person's eyes might slide past her in a crowded room as other more vibrant personalities claimed their attention, but their gaze would eventually come to rest on her, and when it did, Lucas had the disconcerting feeling that they might never look at anyone else ever again.

There he went again, being all whimsical. It must be all this fresh air – he wasn't used to it and it was addling his brain. Maybe he'd grown accustomed to a certain level of pollution and the lack of it was making him have odd thoughts.

Giving himself a mental shake, he clambered to his feet and checked everything was still working by jogging on the spot before continuing with his run. He'd try to keep his mind on what he was doing from now on.

But after several more miles he realised it was impossible, especially since his feet had taken him along Gracie's street on his way home.

How had she got under his skin so quickly and so thoroughly, when he hardly knew anything about her?

He needed to prise her out of his mind, because she couldn't remain in there hijacking his thoughts. His mum was right – at some point he'd return to London and Gracie would stay here. There couldn't be a future for them.

He'd have to withdraw the offer of lunch next Sunday. If his mum had read Gracie correctly, then he needed to knock it on the head. And not just for Gracie's sake. There was no way he could allow himself to get attached. He had enough emotional issues to work through with his mum, his sister and his niece. But he could return to London and his life there without too much heartache at leaving them, and as long as he repaired the damage he'd done then he'd be able to cope with living so far away.

However, not living near his family was one thing – trying to conduct a long-distance romantic relationship was another. It was better to stop this now before it started. Before his mother got any more ideas. Before anyone got hurt. It was all well and good for her to say she wanted him to settle down, but if he was unable to find anyone in a city like London with all those millions of people, he was hardly likely to find someone in a little place like Applewell.

He admitted he fancied Gracie, but that was as far as it went. Anyway, he wasn't the settling down type. His relationships rarely lasted more than a couple of months, partly because of his lack of commitment, and partly because his girlfriends didn't like the way Lucas rubbed shoulders with so many wealthy or famous people without inviting them along. As far as he was concerned, he didn't want his work life and his private life to mix.

Settle down indeed, he scoffed silently as he let himself into his mum's house. A chance would be a fine thing! He had to meet someone first.

It didn't occur to him until much later that he might already have...

Chapter 20

Gracie

'Did you have a good weekend?' Catrin smirked as she opened UnderCover and let Gracie in at eight thirty on Monday morning.

Gracie rolled her eyes. 'I went for a walk. No big deal. Here.' She handed her friend a bag.

'It's not the walk, it's who you went on it with.' Catrin removed the red coat from the bag and examined it. 'Ooh, wonderful! You can't tell it's been repaired.'

'That's the point.' Gracie's tone was dry.

Catrin checked the skirt over, opening and closing the zip, and gave her a smile. 'Thanks, my lovely. Have you got time for a cuppa?'

'Why not. I doubt there'll be a queue outside my shop itching to get their hands on my new range of key rings.' She trailed after Catrin who was heading for the back of the shop.

'Flick the switch on the kettle while I put these away,' Catrin said.

Gracie did as she was told, then watched Catrin slip the coat onto a hanger and ease the hook through a hole she made in the bottom of a large black bag to act as a protective cover. She did the same with the skirt, then hung both items at the back of a rail which held other wintery clothing.

'I'll bring this lot out when we get the first cold snap,' Catrin said. 'You ought to see the lovely boots someone donated last week. I wanted them myself but they're too small.' She eyed Gracie's feet. 'They might fit you.'

'Don't get them out now,' Gracie said. 'I can't think about autumn yet.'

'Because your mind is too full of Lucas?' Catrin teased.

'It most certainly isn't.'

'You've gone red.'

'It's the heat.'

'Pull the other one,' Catrin chortled. 'Tell me all about it – I'm not letting you out of the shop until you do.'

'There's nothing to tell. We walked to the cove and back, then had lunch at his mum's.'

'Ah, I see, that makes sense if Vivien invited you for lunch.'

'Er, no, Vivien didn't invite me: Lucas did.'

'Curiouser and curiouser.' Catrin's expression was avid as she made the tea then sank down onto a hard plastic chair.

Gracie took her mug with a smile and also sat down. 'It was just lunch.'

'Yeah, right...'

'It's not like that, honestly.'

Catrin's expression was doubtful. 'I think it is,' she said. 'You really fancy him, don't you?'

'He's a good-looking man.'

'That's not what I mean, and you know it. Even I can see he's a handsome chappie, but I don't *fancy* him.'

'Honestly, I don't know how I feel,' Gracie admitted. 'Anyway, it's pointless thinking about it; he'll be off back to London soon, so I can't let myself develop any feelings for him.'

Catrin examined her. 'I suspect you already have.'

So did Gracie, but if she kept telling herself she didn't feel anything for him she might believe it. 'What's the news with you and Gareth?'

'Stop trying to change the subject.'

'He's still adamant he wants a break?'

Catrin nodded, her head bowed. When she looked up she had tears in her eyes. 'I keep wanting to burst into tears every five minutes, and I feel sick all the time. The tension at home is awful. I wish he'd just get on with it and move out.'

'Maybe he's waiting for you to do that?'

'Why should I? He's the one who wants to end it, therefore he should be the one to find somewhere else to live.' She scowled. 'If only we didn't have a mortgage, it would make everything much easier. I suppose we'll have to sell up at some point.'

'Are you sure you won't get back together?'

'It doesn't look like it.' She made a choked noise. 'What gets me is that neither of our lives have changed, apart from us not sleeping in the same bed. He's still doing the same things he's always done. Yesterday he went to watch the footie with his mates, and I popped round to my mum's. We did the same bloody thing we always do. He's not exactly spreading his wings, is he?'

The shop door rattled and Catrin leapt to her feet. 'Damn! I'd better open up.' She hesitated and a grin spread across her face. 'I bet that's lover-boy.'

Gracie felt herself redden again, and she prayed it wasn't. Applewell was small so it was to be expected that she'd bump into Lucas regularly, but she seemed to be bumping into him more than she would have thought possible. Or maybe it only seemed that way because she was so aware of him?

Of course it was Lucas at the door. It had to be. Fate was having a great time throwing them together, Gracie complained silently to herself, until she realised that her mind was playing games with her – she *knew* he'd been working in UnderCover all last week. Was it too much of a stretch to guess that he might be working here today? She could just as easily have popped round to Catrin's house this evening and given her the repaired items then. Therefore, the only conclusion she could arrive at was that her subconscious was deliberately putting herself in a situation where she'd meet him. Thanks a bunch…

'Hi Lucas,' she said, her tone light, as he walked into the back room and saw her perched on a chair with a mug in her hand.

'Hi.' He smiled at her but didn't meet her eye.

His attention was on something behind her and she glanced over her shoulder, but the only thing there was the waste fabric bin, so Gracie concluded that he preferred to look anywhere other than at her.

'I'd better get going,' she said, handing Catrin her mug. 'Thanks for the tea.'

'Why don't you come to mine after work and we can have a proper chinwag?'

'Um, OK, I'll… er… see you later.' Gracie couldn't get out of UnderCover fast enough. It was perfectly clear that Lucas had no interest in her. The flirting she'd thought he had been doing yesterday must have been wishful thinking on her part, and she must have imagined his hesitation as he ran past her house yesterday evening. She'd been sitting in her chair by the window in her front room, watching the world go by as she cut up material for the new quilt, when she'd spotted him jogging along the pavement, and she could have sworn he'd slowed down a fraction.

Gracie reached her little shop in record time and was surprised to see that she did indeed have a queue. First in line was Lottie Hargreaves with her youngest, Morgan. Behind her was Barbara, and last but definitely not least, was Nora Grainger with Ruby. It seemed Gracie had no chance of getting away from Lucas – if he wasn't there in person, he was there by proxy.

Feeling even more unsettled, Gracie apologised profusely as she opened the shop and hurried inside.

'Lottie, how can I help?' she asked after she'd thrown her bag in the room at the back and shut the door on it.

'I've got a date for you. I know you can't do during the day apart from Sundays, and I don't work weekends myself, but I do run evening classes, so how about a week Tuesday?'

Lottie was looking at her expectantly and it took Gracie a second to realise what she was referring to. 'Oh, yes, of course, the upholstery demonstration. A week Tuesday is fine.'

'Henry has found a dresser for you. He can bring it over tomorrow, and I've asked him to shove the chair on the van that I'd like you to reupholster, if that's OK. I thought you should take a look at it first, and it'll give you an opportunity to see what fabric you might like to use.' Lottie had a tight hold of her son's hand, and he was beginning to squirm and wriggle. 'I'll call in after Henry's dropped the stuff off and we can firm things up then.' She smiled down at the little boy. 'I won't have this monster with me, so we can chat in peace.'

Gracie said goodbye, then turned to Barbara. 'It's all done,' she said, reaching for the christening gown on one of the shelves under the table.

She was conscious of Nora and Ruby moving closer as she opened the box, and she carefully lifted the gown out of its layers of tissue paper. Gently, she passed it to Barbara, who turned it over in her hands.

'These panels look like they are meant to be there,' the woman said, wonderment in her voice. 'You're so clever. Thank you! Look.' She showed the gown to Nora. 'My grandson is being christened, but my son and his girlfriend left it so long that he's grown too big to fit into this, but Gracie has done wonders with it. If you didn't know it had been altered, you never would have guessed.'

Barbara saw Ruby's fascination and she bent down so the little girl could take a closer look.

'Don't touch,' Nora warned her daughter. 'Little hands can be grubby, and I wouldn't want her to mark it,' she explained.

Gracie rewrapped the gown in its tissue paper and slid it into a bag. Once the payment was sorted out and Barbara had left, it was Nora's turn to be served.

'Can you let out my wedding dress if I don't slim into it in time?' she asked. 'I might need to have panels put in it, like you did with Barbara's christening gown.'

'Remind me, when is the wedding?'

'In just over six weeks.'

'You don't look as though you need to lose any weight.' Gracie gazed at her critically. Nora was tall, like Lucas, and had the same dark hair, but she was slender as opposed to Lucas's far more solid frame.

'Believe me, I do. The dress was Granny's and she had an absolutely tiny waist. I've got to lose a few more pounds before I'm able to get into it. Anyway, that's not why I'm here. I wondered if you could alter this.' Nora took a black chiffon dress out of her bag and held it up. 'It's my prom dress. I want to wear it on our honeymoon; we're going on a cruise and on the last night at sea, there's a ball.'

'It's lovely,' Gracie declared. She put out a hand and touched the beading on the bodice. 'Where does it need altering?'

'Around the boobs mostly,' Nora said. 'Since having Ruby, they've changed shape.'

'I'll have to see it on you,' Gracie said, 'but not yet. Shall we wait until a bit nearer the wedding? I'm worried that if I alter it now and you lose more weight, I might have to do it again. The same with your wedding dress.'

'Good idea. How near? I want to give you enough time.'

'A week before should be OK.'

Nora put the gown away. 'I hear you had lunch at Mum's yesterday.'

'That's right.' Gracie couldn't help wondering if that was the real reason for Nora's visit today.

'She says she's invited you to lunch next week, too.'

'She did.'

'She also mentioned something about taking Ruby to the beach in the morning.'

'It was just a thought; a walk before lunch might be nice.' In fact, it might be an idea to cry off. Lucas hadn't seemed too pleased to see her this morning. But she remembered Vivien's face and her not-so-subtle hint that she wanted Gracie to be there.

'Are you and Lucas dating?' Nora asked abruptly.

'It isn't like that. We're just friends.'

Nora took a moment to reply. 'I wouldn't want to see you hurt.'

'Neither would I,' Gracie quipped, trying to keep the conversation light. 'That's why we're just friends. I'll see you on Sunday,' she added, indicating the end of the discussion. She'd go for Vivien's sake – Nora was still as prickly as a hawthorn tree when it came to Lucas, and if in some small way Gracie could help bring brother and sister closer, she would. Being a buffer between the two for a day wouldn't cost her anything other than her time, and at least she'd get a delicious meal out of it. After that, she vowed she'd try to stay out of his way.

How hard could it be?

Chapter 21

Lucas

Lucas hadn't expected to see Gracie in UnderCover this morning, and it threw him a little. For some reason his heart had skipped a beat, and he'd wondered if it had been wise to have drunk a third cup of coffee. He blamed his mum – she was becoming as addicted to the coffee machine as he was, and had persuaded him to have another.

When Lucas saw Gracie and Catrin sitting in the back room, an image of the red coat flashed into his mind, and his gaze had shot to the bin as though he expected to see it in there. He considered mentioning it, but Gracie had leapt to her feet and had rushed off before he'd had an opportunity to say anything. Which, come to think of it, was probably a good thing, as there was a chance he'd come across as accusatory.

He was still thinking about it when Catrin asked, 'You've been here a week now; have you had any insights in how to improve things?'

'Not really.'

'Does that mean you'll go back to London soon?'

'I'll be here for a few more weeks yet.' In fact, he was thinking of staying until after Nora's wedding. If he did, it would mean a break of almost two months. Would Jonas be OK with that?

There was only one way to find out.

Lucas told Catrin he needed to make a phone call, and he stepped outside the shop to do it, wanting to speak to Jonas in private.

Jonas's greeting was warm, making Lucas feel terrible for even considering so much time away from his job. Technically, he had three more weeks of paid holiday entitlement left. Would Jonas be happy for him to take another month off?

'Without pay, of course,' Lucas added after he'd asked.

'Take whatever time you need,' Jonas said kindly, and Lucas felt awful. He was letting Jonas and the charity down, but the thought of going back to London filled him with dread. He simply wasn't ready. It wasn't anything he could put his finger on, and he didn't think he could put it into words, but whenever he thought of his life there, all he felt was a worrying emptiness. He couldn't face going back. He'd felt more fulfilled this past week, than he'd felt for a long time. Oddly, he also felt closer to Effron in Applewell.

'We'll call it bereavement leave,' Jonas was saying. 'Look after yourself, Lucas, and don't come back to work until you're ready. But promise me you *will* come back? You're too valuable to lose. Thanks for the report you sent through, by the way.'

'It's the least I can do. Will you get someone to chase it up?'

'Leave it with me. We can manage. I don't want you to think about work – you're supposed to be taking a break.'

'You know me, I don't do holidays.'

'Maybe you should? I know we agreed you'd take a look at the business from the retail side of things, but you've got to give yourself time to grieve. I know how close you and Effron were.'

'I've been helping out in the shop in Applewell,' Lucas said, nodding to Donald Mousel who was lingering nearby. Lucas turned his back on the pensioner and lowered his voice. 'It's fun.'

Jonas chuckled. 'If you think that's fun, you need to get out more,' he said, then he sighed. 'You're not going to listen to me, are you? You're going to carry on working regardless of what I say.'

'I'd be bored if I didn't. There's not a great deal to do in Applewell.'

'I thought that was the point. You're supposed to be relaxing: go for a long walk, sit on the beach, read…'

He'd taken a walk and he'd sat on the beach. And he'd be doing the same again next Sunday. As for reading, did spread-sheets count?

It was only after the call had ended, that Lucas realised he hadn't actually promised Jonas he'd go back. He hadn't said anything at all about returning to London and the job he used to love. After all, he didn't want to make a promise he mightn't be able to keep.

–

'Do you want anything while I'm out?' Lucas asked Catrin later that day. She was checking that all five hundred pieces of a jigsaw puzzle were there.

'No, thanks.' She smiled up at him, and started to count. 'One, two, three…'

He left her to it and headed out of the door, hoping she wouldn't get too many interruptions. He'd hate for her to get to four hundred and something, and for a customer to ask her a question – she'd have to start all over again!

The shop had been busy this morning and Catrin had given him job after job to do. He'd just finished steaming a very nice men's suit and thinking that he must remember to check the garment's label on the internet when he got a chance because he was convinced it was designer, when he'd realised how hungry he was.

It was well past his usual lunchtime and Catrin had eaten her sandwiches ages ago, so no wonder he was peckish. He'd pop into Eleri's cafe for a bite to eat rather than grab something to take back to the shop because he could do with a break from it for half an hour or so.

He was contemplating the menu and wondering if it would be greedy to have both the honey mustard pork *and* the cheesy green beans, when a familiar voice made him look up.

Gracie was at the counter, ordering her own lunch, and a smile crept over his face. He didn't mean it to – it happened of its own accord. She had that effect on him.

As though she knew she was being stared at, she glanced over her shoulder and saw him. He must have been grinning like an idiot because a frown creased her forehead for a moment, and he hastily rearranged his own features into a less manic smile. After a second she smiled back, then turned her attention to Eleri who was serving her. But when she looked for a free table, he caught her eye again. The cafe was busy with people enjoying afternoon cake and pots of tea, plus a couple of late lunchers like him and Gracie, and there wasn't an empty table to be found. His had a seat going spare, so he patted it and she raised her eyebrows.

Gracie hesitated, scanned the room again, then headed for his table.

He pushed the chair out for her to sit down, and as soon as she was seated he signalled to Eleri that he was ready to order.

'What are you having?' he asked Gracie.

'A baked potato tuna melt.'

'Sounds good. Hi, Eleri, could I have that too, please, and a side order of cheesy green beans?'

'Coming right up.' Eleri winked at him.

What was all that about, he mused, then immediately forgot as he focused on Gracie. 'I was going to ask if you come here often, but I already know that you do,' he teased.

'It beats warming something up in the microwave later,' she said. 'I hate cooking.'

'I gathered that. I quite enjoy it. I'll have to make my spicy meatballs for you one day.'

'Please don't feel obliged. It was very kind of your mum to invite me for lunch again.'

Lucas laughed. 'Kindness didn't come into it. Did you see her face? She wants you to play referee. Nora's turned into a really feisty woman.'

'She was in my shop earlier.'

'Oh? What did she want?' The babysitting thing wasn't going to happen any time soon, so he owed her a gift and, as she'd been dismissive of the flowers he'd given their mum, maybe Gracie could point him in the right direction.

'Her prom dress altering.'

'She's going to a *prom*?'

'She's going on a cruise for her honeymoon.'

Lucas wasn't any the wiser.

'On the last night at sea there's a ball, and she wants to wear her prom dress,' Gracie explained. 'It's good that she gets a second wearing out of it. Most people either sell theirs or give them away.'

'I fully approve,' Lucas said. 'How could I not, considering I'm helping out in one of UnderCover's shops!'

'How is that going?' She leant back as Eleri appeared with their food. 'Thanks,' she smiled up at her.

'Enjoy your meal,' Eleri said with a smirk and another wink in his direction. Wait, maybe it wasn't a wink, but a tic. Or an eyelash might be irritating her.

'It's going good. I'm surprised at how much I'm enjoying it,' he replied.

Gracie sent him a doubtful look. 'You must miss the hustle and bustle of your job. Philanthropy Manager, you said?'

He was inordinately pleased she remembered. Most people didn't. 'I don't miss it in the slightest,' he confessed and his mood dimmed. 'I'm not looking forward to going back, to be truthful.'

'Everyone feels like that when they're on holiday, but living in Applewell is different from visiting. You must know that...' She delicately placed a morsel of tuna in her mouth and he watched her chew, her lips catching his attention as she licked them.

He had difficulty dragging his gaze away. He'd yet to taste his food, so he tried to concentrate on that, instead of wondering what it might be like to kiss her.

After eating a forkful, he replied to her question. 'Living in London isn't all it's cracked up to be, either.' His tone was subdued.

'But what about all those famous people you meet? And all the theatres and the restaurants, the galleries and the museums?'

'I don't often get to meet famous people – I usually get to meet the people who work for the famous people. Only occasionally do I bump into them at a party or an event. As for theatres, galleries and museums, there is undeniably plenty to do in London and I admit I do rather like the restaurants. However,' – he held up a finger – 'it's far more expensive to eat out in London than it is here, so I don't do it very often.'

'Is that why you learnt to cook?'

'Not really. I wanted to give something back to the charity that helped me, so I started out by volunteering in the soup kitchens. I was taught how to make beef Stroganoff, shepherd's pie with a cheesy crust, lasagne, and all kind of things, as well as a three course Christmas lunch.'

Gracie stopped eating and put her knife and fork down, and he instantly knew what she was thinking, because he used to think the same thing himself.

'Not eating won't make any difference, you know. People will still go hungry. What *does* make a difference is fund-raising or volunteering, and lobbying parliament and your local council.' He pointed to her plate. 'It's not as though you're buying something frivolous or unnecessary. You have to eat. Your life depends on it.'

'So does theirs,' she said, and he knew she was referring to the homeless people he cared so passionately about. 'I try to do my bit by—'

Gracie halted abruptly as Eleri appeared at their table. 'Do you want me to take your plates?'

'I haven't finished yet,' he said. 'Have you, Gracie?'

Her eyes met his. 'Not yet,' she said, and he nodded his approval.

'I might even have a slice of cake after this,' he said, and Eleri retreated to her counter.

'It does make you feel guilty, though,' Gracie said, picking up her fork once more and tucking in.

Lucas understood completely. 'Do you feel guilty about breathing?' he asked.

'No, but...'

'It's kind of the same thing in that you have to eat in order to survive, and you have to breathe in order to survive. The difference comes if you start spending silly amounts on food that does the same job as something you could buy for a fraction of the price.' He went on to tell her about the $5000 burger.

'It's obscene to charge that amount!' she cried.

'It's obscene to *pay* that amount, but some people do.'

She snorted. 'Those with more money than sense. It's a bit "emperor's new clothes", isn't it? Someone, like an influencer for example, says a thing is a must-have, must-eat, must-see, then suddenly everyone wants it and the price rockets, and all the while many of the people who bought it, or ate it, or visited it are wondering that there might be something wrong with them because they don't think it's as fab as everyone else says it is, but they go along with it because they are scared to speak out in case they look daft.' She paused for a much-needed breath, and he noticed that a spot of indignant colour had appeared on each of her sculpted cheeks, highlighting her freckles.

Looking back with the benefit of hindsight, Lucas would realise that without a shadow of a doubt that it was at this point he fell in love with her.

–

'About Nora's wedding,' Lucas said to his mother later that evening. He'd just asked her if he could stay to see Nora get married, and his mother had been thrilled to bits. 'I don't have anything to wear.'

The nuptials had seemed an abstract event to him until now – it was Gracie mentioning that Nora had been into A Stitch in Time earlier today to have her prom dress altered in preparation for her honeymoon which had brought it home to him. Yeah, he'd also missed seeing his sister wearing that dress the first time, along with seeing her huge baby bump, and the hundreds of other things, large and small that he'd not been in Applewell for.

'I thought that was supposed to be my line?' Vivien said.

'Haven't you got your outfit already?' Should he offer to take her shopping? Maybe she didn't have enough money…? He wasn't able to do much about paying any bills whilst he was living here (he'd offered and had been shot down in flames) but he did ensure the fridge and the cupboards were well stocked. How about if he suggested going shopping, and if she saw something she fancied he could buy it for her? His mother mightn't like the idea, but if he got to the card machine before she did, it would be done and dusted, and he'd happily take the flak afterwards.

'Of course, I have! I bought it the minute Ianto proposed,' Vivien said. 'I'll have to try it on and make sure it still fits. You've only been here two weeks and I can already feel the weight creeping on. It's all that food you keep buying. While I remember, is it you who keeps eating the Coco Pops and Nutella?'

'Yes, why? I thought you'd bought them for me?'

'I bought them because Ruby likes them. You get grown-up stuff, such as the coffee machine.'

'I'll buy her some more next time I'm in the supermarket.'

'No need,' his mother chirped. 'She's been eating your yoghurts and muesli.'

Lucas had been wondering how he'd managed to get through so many yoghurts and a box and a half of muesli. He'd suspected his mum had been eating it. Now he knew.

He smiled to himself when he remembered his reaction on seeing the cereal and Nutella the morning after he'd arrived.

He'd tried to munch his way through the Coco Pops and had smeared Nutella on his toast now and again so as not to hurt his mother's feelings, but they weren't his thing anymore. He barked out a laugh as he realised he needn't have bothered.

'Ruby is more than welcome to help herself,' he said, before something occurred to him. 'When was she here?' He was sorry to have missed her.

'She and Nora popped in about an hour ago.'

'Is Nora deliberately keeping Ruby away from me?'

'I don't think it's a question of Nora keeping her away from you; it's more about letting Ruby get used to the idea she has an uncle.'

'Nora never told her about me, did she?'

Vivien looked him in the eye. 'Why would she? You hardly ever visited, never invited any of us to London, and you only barely managed to make it home when the poor little mite was born. You weren't a part of Ruby's life and it didn't look like you ever would be.'

Lucas had to admit the truth – his mother was right. He couldn't blame Nora for not telling her daughter about a man she'd only met twice and only fleetingly at that. He used to use the excuse that he was too busy – which was true, but only because he wanted to be busy. He'd spend his days in work, and his evenings trawling the city with other volunteers, trying to find beds for the night for those who wanted or needed them: sometimes that wasn't the same thing. Weekends followed the same pattern – work if necessary, and helping in shelters or in the kitchens.

Yet, what good had it ultimately achieved? The number of homeless people continued to rise, and the number of resources continued to fall. He might as well have called himself King Canute and be done with it, for all the difference he made.

'Do you want to tell me why you're really back?' his mother asked.

'Effron died.'

'Oh, love...'

She moved towards him and he stiffened as her arms went round him, then he buried his head in her neck and howled.

It was the first time he'd cried since Effron had slipped quietly away in the hospital. The passing of a person such as he should have been accompanied by something more than numb silence. Lucas hadn't been able to give him any more than that. He'd sat there, watching the life leech out of the man who'd been like a father to him, consumed by grief so intense it stole his breath, and he'd not shed one single tear.

'There, there, let it all out,' Vivien crooned, patting his back.

Through his snuffling he dimly registered that she smelt the same as she had when he was a boy. Her hug was the same, too, despite their reversal in size. He dwarfed her physically, yet she towered over him emotionally.

He felt like a child and for the first time since the idea of running away had entered his stubborn head, he revelled in the feeling.

He'd come home.

Chapter 22

Gracie

'You'll have to try them on,' Gracie told Lucas. 'If you want me to do a proper job you can't expect me to guess.'

He was standing in the middle of a Stitch in Time and was holding a pair of suit trousers in front of him and gazing at her hopefully. 'I see. Um, OK... do you have a fitting room?'

'Not really. You can change in the loo, but I must warn you, it's a bit cramped.' Cramped was an understatement. She didn't think Lucas would fit in her tiny loo, and if he wanted to swap trousers he'd most likely get stuck. When an image leapt into her head of her trying to wrestle a half-naked Lucas out of her loo, her tummy did a slow roll and she swallowed nervously. 'I can come to yours after I close, if you like? Or you could come to mine.'

'Mum is meeting her knitting circle tonight and it's her turn to host it, so could I come to yours?' he asked.

Her vision of him in the tiny toilet in the shop was swiftly replaced by an image of him getting changed in her front room. Neither was doing much for her composure.

'About seven?' she squeaked. She cleared her throat and tried again. 'Will seven o'clock be OK?'

'Seven will be perfect.' His eyes lit up. 'What if I bring a takeaway? Do you like Indian? I fancy a curry.'

'Um, yes, that would be great.' Her mouth watered at the thought. She rarely ate curry from a proper Indian restaurant, and she was salivating already.

165

'I've got something else that needs altering, too.' Lucas lifted a suit jacket from the bag at his feet and shrugged it on.

Gracie giggled. It fitted him across the shoulders but she could hardly see his hands sticking out of the sleeves, and it reminded her of a kid who had been forced to wear his taller brother's blazer to school. 'Where did you get it?' she demanded, her amusement threatening to overspill into a proper belly laugh.

'UnderCover. I'd like to meet the fella who used to own it – he's about my build but with much longer arms and legs. My guess is that it's handmade.'

Gracie moved closer so she could examine it.

Lucas was wearing a citrusy cologne with woody undertones. She tried not to sniff him as she took the lapel between her fingers and turned it over. 'I think you're right; it is a made-to-measure suit.' She grasped his hand in order to study the stitching on the inside of the cuff, and felt a jolt go through her at her boldness.

His skin was warm, his hands dwarfing hers, and when she tucked the cuff in on itself to get a view of how it might look with a couple of inches shaved off, her fingers encountered the sparse soft hairs on his forearm, and she shivered at the feel of them.

This was far too intimate for her liking and she hurriedly stepped back, her face flushed.

My goodness, it wouldn't be a good idea to get so close to him again.

Thankfully, Lucas seemed oblivious to the effect he was having on her. 'It's for Nora's wedding,' he said. 'I'm going to stay in Applewell until she gets married.'

Gracie's heart lifted to know that he wasn't going home just yet.

He continued, 'I've got a really good suit back at my flat, but I don't want to go fetch it because...' Lucas ground to a halt.

'Because you think if you returned to London, you might stay there?' she guessed.

166

'I wouldn't intend to, but it's all too easy to slip into old habits. I wouldn't be able to resist checking the old haunts, and that would be that.'

'I take it you're not ready to go home?'

Lucas winced. 'Home is a word I've always associated with Applewell, not London,' he said. 'Not yet.'

Six weeks, maybe slightly less if he took off immediately after the wedding, and he'd be gone – out of her life as fast as he'd entered it. She didn't want to think about it. In a short amount of time she'd got used to seeing him around.

Don't get too used to it, she warned herself, then proceeded to ignore her own warning by thinking about this evening and the meal they would share.

She was in the throes of imagining him feeding her morsels of chicken pasanda from his own fork, when a blaring horn made her jump.

Glancing out of the window, she recognised Henry Hargreaves climbing out of the driver's seat of a van with the council logo splashed on its side.

'Excuse me for a second, I need to see a man about a dresser.' Gracie went to the door and wedged it open. She'd already made room for it along the back wall, and she checked to make sure the path was clear for Henry to bring it in.

She went outside and joined Henry at the back of the van, aware that Lucas had followed her. She fully expected him to say goodbye and return to UnderCover, but instead he lingered.

'Hi, Henry, thanks for bringing it,' she said, impatient for him to unlock the rear doors so she could get a look at it.

'No worries. You've got a helper, I see,' he said, giving Lucas a nod. 'Good job, too, because it's on the heavy side and it's going to be awkward to get it through that door.' He gave her shop door a frown.

'Oh, Lucas isn't here to help, he's—'

'Happy to give you a hand,' Lucas said, stepping forward and holding out his right one. 'Lucas Grainger.'

Henry took it and the two men shook. 'Henry Hargreaves. Nice to meet you at last.'

Gracie bit her lip and shot Lucas a swift look, not knowing how he'd react to this latest evidence of the Applewell gossip machine in action.

To her relief he didn't appear perturbed.

'What needs doing?' he asked Henry, who threw the van's doors open.

'This needs putting in there,' Henry said.

'It's gorgeous!' Gracie declared when she saw the dresser. It was big, too, just as Henry had warned. It had three cupboards on the bottom section, with three drawers, and the top was a shelf unit, and all of it was painted a lovely shade of mushroom, with cute knobs and cup hooks hanging from one of the shelves.

'I bet it didn't look like this when you first saw it,' Gracie guessed, knowing that the paint job, the knobs, and probably the cup hooks were down to Lottie.

'It didn't,' Henry laughed. 'I was told to bring you this chair, too.' He pointed to an old armchair with a high back. It had a padded back and seat, and the arms also had a small amount of padding over them. It had cracked gilding on all the exposed wood, and the material it was covered in was in a bit of a state, threadbare and faded. Gracie suspected the ticking would be original and would also need replacing. It wasn't a five-minute job, but neither would it be too arduous or complicated, and she looked forward to getting stuck in.

She noticed Lucas's doubtful look, and she guessed he must be wondering how the dresser and the chair were both going to fit into her small shop.

'The dresser is going along the back wall,' she explained, 'and the chair is a reupholstery project. Lottie, Henry's wife, upcycles and repurposes old furniture, and she's asked me to do an upholstery demonstration for one of the classes she runs. Are you sure you don't mind helping unload the dresser?' she asked.

'Not at all.'

'In that case,' she said to Henry, 'I can dig out some fabric that I think might work and you can take the chair and the material back to Lottie's workshop. It'll save you having to come back for it.' There was no way the chair would fit in Gracie's car.

She left the men to it and went inside to look through her stock of fabrics. As well as reusing any fabric she could get her hands on, she also sold pieces of reclaimed material, plus buttons, zips, toggles, and anything else she salvaged. It wasn't unusual to see someone rooting through her jars of buttons to find a replacement for one that had come off and got lost.

'Here you go,' she said to Henry, handing him several swathes of fabric once the dresser was in position. 'Any of these would look good. Ask Lottie which one she wants to use, and we'll go from there. She's popping in later, so she can bring back any that she doesn't like.'

'Will do.'

'Do I owe you anything?' Gracie asked. 'The dresser on its own has got to be worth more than an upholstery demonstration, and then there's the work Lottie has put into it.'

'Nope. It was in bits when it arrived at the recycling centre so it couldn't be resold in the tip shop anyway. And Lottie used it to show her students how to repair drawers and rehang doors and whatnot.' He left with a cheery goodbye and a promise to pass on her thanks to Lottie.

Gracie would thank Lottie herself later.

She turned her attention to Lucas who was looking at the dresser, his head cocked to the side.

'Did I understand correctly – you swapped this for a demonstration?'

'That's right. It's called bartering.' She picked up one of the bowls she'd made and tipped some scrunchies into it, then placed it on a shelf. 'The last time I bartered, I made curtains and a duvet set for Lottie, Lottie made an old TV cabinet into a play kitchen for Eleri's cafe, and Eleri gave me a week's worth of meals.' Another bowl would be good for displaying the key rings. Customers loved to root through to find a design they liked, and each one was unique. 'Tell a lie, I've been doing something similar with Ca— Damn!'

As she was about to put the bowl on the shelf, she knocked the edge and the key rings spilt over the floor.

She crouched down and began retrieving them, hoping none of them had slid under the dresser: it would be a nuisance to move.

'Let me help.' Lucas dropped to his knees and picked some up, so close to her that if she was brave enough all she needed to do was to turn her head and she'd be kissing him.

As if he sensed what she was thinking, he looked up and their eyes met.

Time stopped and Gracie's heart stilled.

Her hand, in the middle of reaching for a blue patterned key ring with the letter M on it, trembled slightly.

Did she dare? She hesitated...

She didn't dare – but *Lucas* did.

Slowly he leant forward. His breath was warm, his eyes pools of darkness. As his lips fluttered against hers, Gracie's only thought was that she hadn't expected their first kiss to take place on the floor of her shop.

Then all thought ceased as she lost herself in the moment.

It felt as though it lasted for hours, but it couldn't have done – there hadn't even been any tongue-action. As he drew away, she went with him, reluctant for the kiss to end, until she felt close to toppling over and she sank onto her heels and let out the softest of despondent sighs.

Her eyes bored into his as she tried to read the emotion in them. Did he regret what had just happened? Was he not bothered? Did he actually feel anything at all, or was this commonplace for him?

'I feel I should apologise,' he said. 'But I'm not going to.'

Gracie licked her lips, and she noticed the way his gaze dropped to her mouth. 'There's no need.'

'I want to kiss you again.'

The bell above the door tinkled. 'Now is not the best time,' she murmured.

'Pity.'

'Coo-ee!' a voice called. 'Anyone in?'

'I'm down here,' Gracie said, holding onto the table and getting unsteadily to her feet. She turned to see Mrs Mousel peering at her.

Mrs Mousel's eyes nearly popped out of her head when Lucas unfurled himself to stand next to Gracie. She looked from him, to her, then back to him again.

'I… er… dropped…' Gracie held up the half-full bowl of key rings. She said to Lucas, 'I can manage from here. Thanks for the help.' Please don't mention this evening, she prayed silently as he handed her the key ring he was holding. Gracie held it up for Mrs Mousel to see.

'See you at seven,' he said, and Gracie felt like kicking him. 'What should I get you? I think I'll have lamb bhuna.'

'Chicken pasanda, please.' She forced the words out between clenched teeth, conscious of Mrs Mousel's scrutiny.

'Naan bread? Rice?'

'I don't mind. Whatever you're having.' She wished he'd leave. The news that they were seeing each other later would be all over Applewell within the hour.

'Will you be needing a taxi?' the elderly woman asked, fishing for info.

'No thanks, Mrs Mousel,' Gracie said, ushering Lucas towards the door.

'Donald could take you and fetch you, if you want, so both of you could have a drink?'

'We don't need a taxi, thanks all the same.' Gracie lowered her voice as she reached the door. 'Go,' she hissed to Lucas. 'Escape while you can.'

With his sexy laugh making her breath catch in her throat, Gracie pushed him outside, his parting shot of 'Later', sounding like a promise of more kissing to come.

'Right, Mrs Mousel, what can I do for you?' Gracie asked, her pulse returning to normal as she turned her attention to her customer.

'Tony mentioned that you'd just had a big item delivered, so I thought I'd pop in and ask if you needed any help.'

'That's very kind of you, but as you can see it's all done.'

'That nice Lucas Grainger helped, did he?'

'Yes, he did. Actually, if you really want to give me a hand, you can help me pick the rest of these up,' Gracie suggested.

It was at that point that Mrs Mousel suddenly remembered she had to be somewhere urgently, leaving Gracie chuckling to herself as the woman hurried out of the shop.

Living in Applewell was certainly amusing.

Chapter 23

Lucas

Lucas wasn't entirely sure why he'd kissed Gracie. Apart from fancying her, enjoying being with her and finding it hard not thinking about her when he wasn't, he had absolutely no reason to kiss her. She'd not given him the slightest hint that she was attracted to him, and there was also the added issue that in a few short weeks he'd be heading back to London and out of her life. Not only that, he had been warned not to get involved with her.

He should heed the advice. It wasn't fair on Gracie to love her and leave her. Not that he had any intention of jumping into bed with her (no matter how much he wanted to), but even kisses could lead to an involvement that would be hard to break. He didn't want to hurt her, but neither did he want to be hurt himself, and he had the feeling he might be if he carried on seeing her. She'd not only got under his skin, she was burrowing her way into his heart, and he dreaded to think of the damage she might do once she got there.

It occurred to him that it might be too late and the damage was already done, but he dismissed it. He'd only known her for two weeks for goodness' sake, and such fanciful notions wouldn't do anyone any good, least of all him. He didn't do fanciful. He was realistic and streetwise and didn't believe it was possible to fall for someone at the drop of a hat. These things took time, surely?

Nevertheless, he was terribly excited about seeing her this evening, and it had nothing to do with her altering the suit he'd bought from UnderCover. He'd paid more than it was probably worth: it might be handmade but there weren't many men around who were as broad-shouldered as its original owner and fewer still who were as tall, and that included Lucas himself; he was six-foot-two, and he estimated the suit had been made for a man who was at least six-foot-five. Not only were there fairies at the bottom of Ruby's garden, but there must be giants in Applewell, too.

Better too long than too short, Lucas mused as he perused the menu of the nearest Indian takeaway. At least too long could be shortened. He'd look daft if the trousers had been flapping about his ankles and the sleeves halfway to his elbows.

Oh, my God! He hoped Gracie wouldn't have to measure his inside leg! If she did, he'd want to do far more than kiss her. If she suggested it, he'd talk her out of it. There was no way he could survive the embarrassment. Or the desire he'd undoubtedly feel.

As soon as the meal arrived, Lucas was out of the door and striding along the street. For one thing, his mum's friends had just arrived and he was glad to escape; and for another, he couldn't wait to see Gracie. That brief brush of the lips had been one of the most delicate and erotic kisses he'd ever experienced. Who knew that kneeling on a floor in a shop could lead to such a profound experience.

'Get over yourself,' he muttered, earning a sideways look from a man walking his dog. Profound indeed! He was talking rubbish. It was a quick kiss, that's all. There was nothing earth-shattering about it. In fact, it had been damned uncomfortable kneeling on the hard floor and leaning towards her. He'd thought at one point that he was about to lose his balance. Gracie almost had, he recalled. As he'd pulled back, his knees creaking as though they belonged to a man in his nineties, he'd almost unbalanced her.

It hadn't stopped him from wanting to kiss her again immediately though, and he could have cursed the untimely arrival of a customer. Thankfully, Gracie seemed to want him to kiss her just as much. At least, she hadn't slapped his face.

When she answered the door, he could tell she was nervous. She gave him a shy smile then focused on the carrier bag in his hand as she took it from him. He followed her into the kitchen.

'Do you want to eat first, or will you be too full afterwards?' she asked.

It took him a second to realise she meant that he might be too full to try on his suit, not that he'd be too full for anything more energetic. And pleasurable.

That wasn't why he was here, he remonstrated silently and told himself to think of anything else other than kissing her and what it might lead to.

Anyway, no matter how turned on he was, he wasn't in the habit of leaping into bed with a woman the first chance he got. Despite being a healthy red-blooded male, he first liked to get to know the person he hoped to be intimate with. And although he felt he knew Gracie a little, he didn't know her nearly as well as he wanted.

'Eat first,' he said, realising she was waiting for an answer.

'Good, I'm starving. I didn't go to the cafe today in case I was tempted to eat something more substantial than a sandwich. I didn't want to spoil my appetite.'

She unpacked the bag, carefully lifting out cartons and placing them on the counter. The smell was amazing, and his stomach growled. He hoped she liked what he'd bought, and he thought they might share, but at least she could eat the pasanda, naan bread and rice, if she didn't fancy what he'd chosen.

'Grab some plates out of the cupboard above your head,' she instructed, and when he got them out she indicated he should put them on the table.

'I've got wine. Would you like a glass?' she offered.

'Why not!' He'd only have the one glass, though, because he wanted to go to UnderCover in the morning, and he also didn't want to get squiffy in Gracie's presence and do something he'd regret – like grab her around the waist and kiss her until she begged for mercy.

'This is nice,' Gracie said when they were both seated with a glass of wine at hand and various cartons of food laid out on the table. 'I don't usually have guests. Except Catrin, and she doesn't count.'

'Are you two close?'

'I suppose we are.' Gracie's head was bowed over her plate, so he couldn't see her expression clearly. 'She understands me.' Gracie looked up. 'I can be a bit introverted.'

Lucas smiled softly at her. 'You don't say?'

'Is it that obvious?'

'Only if you're looking for it.'

'Have you been looking?' She peered at him from underneath her lashes.

'Yes,' he answered honestly, 'I have.'

'I wish you wouldn't.'

'I like looking at you.'

Her head was down again, and she was staring intently at her plate. He reached across the table, put a finger under her chin and gently tilted her face up until she was looking at him. 'Don't be shy,' he said. 'You're beautiful.' He withdrew his hand, hoping she wouldn't drop her head again.

She didn't. 'I've got freckles.' Her eyes were darker than he remembered, and so large and luminous he thought he might fall in and never find his way out.

He chuckled softly. 'I know.'

'And frizzy hair.'

'What's wrong with that? Come to think of it, what's wrong with freckles? I think they're lovely. *You're* lovely.'

She didn't say anything, but she continued to stare at him with those kitten eyes, her expression solemn.

'Let's eat, before it gets cold,' he said, sensing her discomfort, and he picked up his fork, pretending to concentrate on his food, when in reality all he could think about was her.

How could she not know how beautiful she was? She might have freckles and wild exuberant hair. She might be short and delicate. She might be introverted and shy. But she was the most arresting woman he had ever met.

They ate in relative silence, but gradually as the level in the wine bottle went down, the conversation increased, until she was happily laughing at the stories he told her regarding the people he had to schmooze, and how difficult and downright annoying some of them could be. He wasn't normally in the habit of sharing such things, but as long as he didn't let slip anything that would identify anyone, it was worth it to see the mirth on her face.

'Of course,' he finished up, 'it doesn't matter how many hoops I have to jump through to get a donation, as long as they do actually donate. Keeping the charity going is my only concern.'

Gracie got to her feet and began clearing away the remains of their meal. 'That was lovely. How much do I owe you?'

'Nothing.' Lucas was shocked. 'I suggested it, and I don't expect you to contribute anything. It's my treat.' Suddenly the awkward atmosphere was back, and he couldn't understand why.

'I'd prefer to go halves,' she said.

'Would you say the same if I asked you out on a date?'

'Probably.'

'By "probably" you mean "yes", don't you?'

Her lips twitched. 'Yes. How much do I owe you?'

He thought furiously. 'How much are you going to charge for taking up my suit?'

She frowned. 'I wasn't going to charge you at all,' she admitted, and he barked out an incredulous laugh.

'You've got a business to run,' he pointed out.

'But it will only take me half an hour,' she objected.

'I don't care. If you don't let me pay you for your time, then you're not getting your hands on my trousers. I'll wear the suit as it is.'

'You'll look ridiculous.'

'Yes, I will.'

'You can't go to Nora's wedding like that. She'll have your guts for garters.'

'Undoubtedly.'

Stalemate. 'Tell you what,' he said, 'if you don't insist on paying half for the food, I won't insist on paying you for the alterations to the suit. Do we have a deal?' He'd find some other way of paying her for her sewing skills, even if it meant he had to send his mother into the shop to buy half of Gracie's stock.

'Lucas Grainger, are you bartering with me?'

'I most certainly am.'

'OK, then.'

He let out a whoop. 'Yes, I win!'

'No, you don't. We both win. Now, do you want to change into the suit, so I can uphold my end of the bargain?'

'Where shall I change?'

'The bathroom is upstairs.'

Lucas carried his second-hand suit up the stairs, taking a quick peep into one of the bedrooms on the way. It was white. Totally white. And when he looked at the bed, the vision of colourful Gracie lying across it, with her boisterous hair and her dappled skin, was so intense it staggered him.

Getting changed took him longer than it should have done because that vision wouldn't go away, and he was worried at the effect it was having on him. There was no way he could be near her with that image in his head. He'd never be able to look her in the face again if his body reacted to her the way he feared it might.

After furiously trying to list all the teams in the football world cup and their star players (which was a challenge because he didn't really care about football) he was finally ready to go downstairs.

Gracie was waiting for him in the lounge. She was kneeling on the floor in the middle of the room, her hands on her knees, a tape measure and a pin cushion next to her.

'Come here,' she said, patting the carpet in front of her. Her voice was husky, and he hastily began to list football strikers in his head.

Standing awkwardly, he shuffled from foot to foot until she slapped his toes.

'Keep still! How do you expect me to pin this up evenly if you're hopping up and down?'

'Don't exaggerate.'

'If you keep bouncing around, this will take all night.'

Yes, please. 'You're still exaggerating. I'm not bouncing. I'm just trying to get my balance.'

'You have both feet planted firmly on the floor. How can you lose your balance?'

The way his head was swimming, he didn't know how he was managing to remain upright. Her bowed head was at the level of his knees, and he could smell her perfume, a sweet floral scent which suited her perfectly.

'This must have cost a fair bit when it was made,' she said, somewhat indistinctly, and when she raised her head he realised why, as she had several pins in her mouth. 'The material is gorgeous, and the amount of work that has gone into it...' She carried on talking about types of stitches or seams – he wasn't sure which – but he wasn't really listening; he was too busy trying to remember how many goals had been scored in the final. Was it three, or four?

'Are you listening to me?' She poked him in the ankle. Luckily it was with her finger and not a pin. 'I said, you could have sold this suit for a fortune online. OK, maybe not a fortune,' she amended when he didn't say anything. 'But more than you paid for it in the shop. I've seen the prices that UnderCover charges, and they don't take whether it's designer into account. Or if they do – I know Catrin has charged more for some things – as a customer you've got to be in the shop at the right time, and it's got to be the right size and in the right colour. I know that's true for everything in UnderCover, but if a dress is marked up at say £100 because it's a Valentino, it'll probably be bought by someone who intends to sell it on rather than wear it themselves, and for a lot more money.'

Gracie stopped talking.

She was staring past his legs, her gaze unfocused.

'Do you sell designer stuff online?' she asked.

'I'm not sure.'

'What about vintage clothes?'

'I honestly don't know.' Why was she talking about this when all he could think about was kissing her?

Gracie rose fluidly to her feet. 'I suggest you find out, because all those designer and vintage pieces that are donated to UnderCover could make a lot more money for the charity if they were sold online. I bet the vast majority are bought to be sold on eBay or Vinted, or by those companies who rent designer clothes out by the week. Imagine if all that profit went directly to UnderCover? You can get changed now; I'm done.'

Lucas began to walk towards the door, anxious to get out of the suit and into his far more comfortable jeans, and also anxious to put some distance between himself and the woman he was desperately trying not to crush to him and kiss soundly.

Abruptly he halted as some of what Gracie had said filtered through his lascivious thoughts.

'I think you might be onto something,' he said. 'Although, it might be expensive to set up and run.'

'It might,' she conceded. 'On the other hand, it might also pay for itself.'

'I'll have to speak to Jonas,' Lucas mused. 'He's in a much better position to see if this suggestion of yours is viable. And he can also get the costings done.'

While in the bathroom he kept thinking furiously as he slipped the suit off and hoisted his jeans back on. It was a good idea of Gracie's, and he wondered whether any of the other charities were already doing it. Whether they were or weren't, if UnderCover decided to go ahead with it, his visit to Applewell would be worthwhile just for that.

This time when he went downstairs she was curled up on the sofa. She'd opened a fresh bottle of wine and two glasses were sitting next to it on the coffee table. Soft music filled the room and her perfume lingered in the air. Her head was resting on the back of the sofa, her eyes were closed, and she was singing quietly, her voice only just audible.

All thoughts of work fled.

Lucas moved silently across the carpet in his stockinged feet, his focus wholly on her and his need to kiss her. Slowly he sat down next to her, so as not to startle her, and when she opened her eyes and stopped singing, he urged her to carry on, suspecting this was a side to her not many people got to see.

Eyes shuttered again, she lost herself in the music once more as he sat and watched her lips move, her chest rise and fall, until the song was done. She'd been singing *Perfect* by Ed Sheeran, and when it was done and the last note had faded away she slowly opened her eyes and turned to look at him. In that moment he realised that's what *she* was: perfect.

He inched across the cushions, until his knee touched hers, then his thigh, and without pause she was in his arms and his mouth claimed hers.

Heart pounding so fast he was scared it would leap out of his chest, Lucas slowly slipped sideways until her body rested on his, and he ran his hands up and down her back until one of them found the tangle of her hair. He buried his fingers in the wild curls and held her to him, his breath hitching in his chest as desire coursed through him.

Several songs later, with their kisses ever more urgent, Gracie dragged her lips from his and sat up. Her hair was a cloud around her shoulders, her pupils large, and her lips dark red and swollen in the fading light. He'd never seen anything more arousing in his life, and the urge to scoop her up and take her to bed was overwhelming.

'We mustn't,' she said. 'I can't.'

He was desperate for her, but a modicum of rational thought remained. She was right; she shouldn't. It was the correct decision to pull away, but he felt desolate. His arms ached without her in them, and his hands still felt the impression of her, the sweep of her spine, the curve of her hip, the swell of her—

'You're right.' He sat up and shuffled back, putting a small but significant distance between them. 'This is moving too fast.'

'It shouldn't be moving at all. You'll be gone soon and I'll…' She gestured to the air. 'I can't do this.'

'I understand.' He really did, and he didn't blame her. Despite his intense desire for her, he also had his own emotional well-being to think of. How could he return to London and leave her behind if their kisses had ended in her bed?

It was going to be difficult enough as it was, and he suspected she'd be on his mind for many months to come, even after he'd slipped back into familiar routines.

Those familiar routines already made his soul ache and his stomach clench, without adding a broken heart into the equation.

And, he strongly suspected, if he made love to Gracie his heart would be well and truly lost.

Little did he know that it already was.

Chapter 24

Gracie

Gracie had never once thought her bed was too big. But last night it had seemed vast and empty, in spite of her starfish attempts to fill it. She usually loved sleeping alone. However, with her mind filled with Lucas, she hated it.

She could easily have taken him to her bed, and she'd have enjoyed every second of it – if his kisses were any indication, she guessed he'd be a considerate lover. But she didn't see the point of inviting heartache into her life. She was going to have enough trouble forgetting him as it was; imagine how much worse it would be if she had made love to him. Gracie wasn't someone who could give her body without giving her heart, and she'd given him a piece of it already.

Anxious to salvage what was left of it, she vowed to be politely friendly when they next met. There could certainly be no more kissing. She'd keep him at arm's length, and try not to think about his arms holding her, or hers curling around his neck. And she definitely wouldn't think about how his tongue had found hers, or her response.

She'd only been in the shop for a few minutes when the first nosey parker came in. She'd kind of expected it, but for it to be Catrin was a surprise.

'You're a dark horse,' her friend said.

'It was a business thing.'

Catrin said, 'Mrs Mousel didn't seem to think so. She told me that the pair of you were on your knees hiding behind the table. And then she heard you making plans to see him last night.'

'It was about the suit. Didn't Lucas try it on in the shop?'

Her friend giggled. 'Yes, he did. He looked as though he was trying on his dad's clothes. I keep racking my brains to think of anyone tall enough who could have donated it.'

'Lucas and I were wondering the same thing. I doubt if we'll ever know.'

'Listen to you, "Lucas and I".' Catrin did air quotes with her fingers around the words.

'You can hardly read anything intimate into that.'

'You've gone all defensive. And you're blushing. If there isn't anything going on between the two of you, you'd like there to be, wouldn't you?'

'I'd like nothing of the sort.'

'Liar. You ought to see your face.'

Gracie pursed her lips, refusing to be drawn.

Caitlin narrowed her eyes. 'You've kissed him, haven't you?'

Gracie looked away. It really was none of Catrin's business.

'Well, well, well.' Catrin moved closer and put her arm around Gracie's shoulders. 'Are you sure about this? He's terribly good-looking, so I don't blame you. If it wasn't for Gareth, I'd probably take a punt on him myself. I know you; you couldn't just do a fling. For you it would have to be something more. But I'll be honest, I don't think Lucas is the type of guy to give anything more. Not only that, but he'll be going back to where he came from soon, and I don't want to see you hurt.'

Gracie didn't want to see herself hurt either. 'He's staying until after his sister's wedding,' she said, as though it made any difference.

'He's still going to leave,' Catrin pointed out gently.

'We're just friends,' Gracie insisted, 'although I think he'd like it to be more.' She *knew* he'd like it to be more, as would she, but she wasn't going to allow that to happen.

'Are you sure you're OK?'

'I'm fine. Honestly.' But she wasn't though: she was already starting to feel the first little cracks appearing in her heart, and she prayed it wasn't a prelude to having it completely shattered.

'How about we go out on Friday?' Catrin suggested.

Gracie thought about it. She also thought about what her friend had just said. Catrin was right: Gracie didn't do holiday romances. And that was what this would be, if she didn't knock it on the head now. It couldn't possibly be anything more. Therefore, the best thing to do would be to avoid him. The less she saw of Lucas, the less she'd be tempted to kiss him, and she might as well put this vow in place today.

'Not The Busy Bumble,' she said.

'There's nowhere else – unless you want to drive, but then you can't have a drink. You can come to mine if you like: I'll get some prosecco in. Is it because you're worried you might bump into Lucas if we go to The Busy Bumble?'

'I'll be seeing enough of him what with doing the alterations on his suit, and I promised to have lunch at his mother's house on Sunday. But after that I'm hoping I won't see him again.'

'Fat chance,' Catrin said. 'Applewell is too small not to.'

'Then I'll just have to hide in my shop or in my house until he buggers off back to London. Let's face it, it won't be much of a hardship because I've been doing that for years.' She might have to change her routine a bit, get up an hour earlier to be in A Stitch in Time before Catrin opened UnderCover, for instance, but she could manage that.

So when twelve noon arrived and she realised she'd forgotten to have breakfast (food had been the last thing on her mind when she'd dragged herself out of bed this morning) she decided to have an early lunch and hopefully the change to her usually very predictable schedule would ensure she didn't bump into Lucas today. If he wanted to pay her a visit in the shop there was nothing she could do about that, but if there were things she could control, she would.

She was peering at the specials board, when a familiar voice said, 'Hello.'

When she spotted him, she did a double-take and her treacherous heart leapt with delight before she forced it to behave itself; she'd give it a good talking to later.

'We must stop meeting like this,' Lucas joked.

'Yes, we must. Hi, Eleri, could I have a kofta and mint dip wrap please, with salad?' Gracie said, trying not to look at him in case her resolve wavered.

'You're early,' Eleri said. 'We don't usually see you before two.'

'Um, yeah, I, er, was hungry.'

'Me, too,' Lucas said. 'That's the odd thing about rice, it fills you up at the time but you're starving the next day.'

Eleri gave Gracie a knowing look.

'I'll have mine to go,' she said. 'Must get back. Got work to do.' She forced each sentence out through stiff lips, ignoring Lucas's crestfallen expression.

Tapping her foot as she waited for Eleri to prepare her lunch, Gracie continued to pretend Lucas wasn't there, which wasn't easy when every cell in her body was urging her to grab him and drag him back to her house. She could smell his aftershave and that underlying scent which was his and his alone. It made the hairs on her arms stand on end, and she shivered at the animal emotion coursing through her.

She couldn't get away from him or her feelings for him, and she wondered if this was what it was going to be like when Lucas returned to London. She'd still be seeing him in the faces of his family, in the cove, in UnderCover, and even in her own shop. He'd be gone, but she wouldn't be able to escape him.

Gracie took a breath, forcing herself to be rational.

As long as she didn't let things go any further between them, as long as she kept a firm grip on herself, she'd be fine. There'd be no harm done. It wasn't as though she was in love with him – in lust, maybe, but once the object of her desire was out of sight, he'd be out of mind. She just needed to keep reminding herself of that.

When Eleri handed her a bag with her lunch in, Gracie took it and hurried off. She didn't even say goodbye to him.

—

'Have I done something to upset you?' Lucas had followed her to A Stitch in Time and those were the first words out of his mouth when he pushed the door open to find her dropping her lunch in the bin, her appetite suddenly vanished.

'No,' she replied tightly.

'Are you sure? Because you seem upset to me.'

She *was* upset, but it was nothing he'd done; she supposed she could take him to task for wanting a holiday fling, but he wasn't doing anything that thousands of other men hadn't done when they were on holiday.

She should have been more mindful of herself and her feelings. If she was hurt, it would be her own fault.

'I'm fine,' she insisted.

There was a strained silence, and Gracie turned her back on him and busied herself with tidying things that didn't need tidying.

Finally, Lucas took the hint and walked out, leaving Gracie alone.

It was something she was awfully familiar with, but which got harder to bear as the years went by.

But bear it she must.

Gulping back tears of self-pity, she did the only thing that might give her a scrap of comfort – she began working on the alterations to Lucas's suit.

Chapter 25

Lucas

Lucas had half-expected to see Gracie in The Busy Bumble on Friday evening but to his disappointment she wasn't there. He hadn't set eyes on her since Wednesday, and he still didn't know what he'd done wrong. More than once over the course of the past two days, he'd been tempted to seek her out and ask her again, but she'd made it clear she didn't want anything to do with him. So he'd taken heed of her wishes and had stayed away. He'd not even popped into the cafe for a bite to eat, not wanting to intrude or to make her feel uncomfortable. Instead, he'd made sandwiches at home and had eaten them in UnderCover, under the curious and rather watchful gaze of the shop's manager.

However, he didn't see why he should live the life of a total hermit, and he desperately needed to get out of the house, which was why he was propping up the bar of The Busy Bumble with a pint in his hand. There were also two other reasons – one being the hope of bumping into Gracie, and the other that he was meeting Ianto.

He wasn't sure which of the two he was most nervous about.

'Hello, again,' Henry Hargreaves said. 'Lottie has let me out for a couple of hours, so I thought I'd grab a beer. How are you?'

'Good, thanks. Let me get these.' Lucas drained his glass and ordered two more beers.

'Cheers.' Henry held his drink aloft before taking a long swallow. After wiping his upper lip, he said, 'How are you enjoying being back in Applewell?'

'It's good. Different.'

'I bet it is. I wouldn't like to live in a city myself. Aberystwyth is busy enough for me, especially in summer.'

'Crumbs, I haven't been there in years.'

'You must pay it a visit, and come and see me while you're at it. I suppose you could say we're in the same line of work, except the money from the tip shop is ploughed into council-run community projects.'

'My main focus isn't recycling,' Lucas explained. 'It's raising money for the charity. I'm not usually involved in the retail side of the organisation. I am enjoying it though.'

'But you'll be going back home soon, right? Back to your proper job?'

'I suppose.'

'You don't sound too sure?'

'I'm sure. I can't stay in Applewell forever.'

'I did.'

'Sorry, that wasn't a criticism. My life is in London – my flat, my job.'

'I didn't take it as such. I just meant that if you are happy here, why not stay?'

Why not, indeed! There were a hundred reasons why not. 'I can't keep volunteering in the shop – Catrin's had enough of me already.'

'Did you say Catrin?' A man standing on Lucas's other side butted in.

'Yes, do you know her?'

'I should do. I live with her. Are you the bloke who wants to do her out of a job?'

Lucas sighed; he'd thought this rumour had been put to bed. 'Not at all. She knows why I'm here. Didn't she tell you?' He gathered he was speaking to Gareth.

'Uh, no.' Gareth looked a little sheepish, and Lucas guessed that there might not be a great deal of amicable conversation in Catrin's house at the moment.

Deciding to feign ignorance that Gareth and Catrin were having relationship issues, Lucas said, 'You're a lucky guy – Catrin is lovely.'

Gareth downed his pint and glared at him.

'Um, Gareth and Catrin have broken up,' Henry said in Lucas's ear.

'Oh, sorry, mate, I didn't realise. When you said you live with her...' Lucas trailed off.

'It's complicated,' Gareth said.

'Life often is,' Lucas said, thinking of his non-existent relationship with Gracie.

'Life is often what?' Ianto asked appearing at Lucas's elbow.

'Complicated,' Lucas said.

Ianto gave him a measured look. 'It certainly is. Anyone up for another pint?'

And that was it, the ice was broken between Lucas and Ianto, and over the course of the evening Lucas was pleased to discover he liked the guy his sister was going to marry. He liked Henry and Gareth too, and he thought how they could easily become friends if he were to remain in Applewell. Not that he was going to, of course. He had a job he loved (*used to love*, a voice in the back of his mind said) and which he'd have to go back to sooner rather than later. He could only rely on Jonas's goodwill for a certain amount of time. There would come a point where that would run out, along with his salary, and he couldn't live on fresh air – he'd been there and done that, and it was hard. So bloody hard.

Besides, he couldn't help UnderCover from Applewell, and the charity was his life. He couldn't imagine working anywhere else. Or what job he could do if he did.

'My round,' Gareth said, and Lucas tried to work out how many he'd drank already, and failed. It had to be at least five. Or was it six? He was lightheaded, and his mouth had lost some feeling – a sure sign he was on the way to being steaming.

'Best not. I've got work in the morning,' he said.

'UnderCover, you mean? Go on, you can have another,' Gareth said. 'Catrin will be there, so you don't have to be.'

'I want to be there. I like it.'

'Or is it Catrin you like?' the man asked, the glare he'd given Lucas earlier returning.

'Don't be daft, man, he likes Gracie,' Henry said. 'Mrs Mousel caught them at it.'

'At what?' Lucas asked, confused.

'You know. Nudge, nudge; wink, wink. In her shop, too. They were hiding under the table.' Henry was doubled over with laughter.

'We were not "at it",' Lucas objected. 'I was helping Gracie pick up some keyrings that had fallen on the floor.'

'You might want to tell that story to Mrs Mousel, because she's been telling everyone a different tale. You can't deny you spent the night with her, though.'

'I can and I do. Mrs Mousel is old enough to be my gran.'

Gareth snorted and some of his drink went up his nose. 'You crease me, you really do,' he spluttered.

Ianto, who appeared to be less drunk than the others, asked, 'Did you spend the night with Gracie?'

'I did not.'

'Did you want to?'

'That's none of your business.'

'Oh, mate, you've got a lot to learn about living in Applewell.'

Lucas tried to tell Ianto that he knew a great deal about living in Applewell and it was one of the reasons he'd left in the first place, but the words refused to come. It all sounded so irrelevant. 'I bought a suit. For your wedding. It's too big,' he said, instead. 'Gracie is altering it. That's why I was at her house. I paid her with a curry.'

Henry clapped him so hard on the back, Lucas almost spilt his drink. 'She's got you into bartering, has she? Gracie is a diamond. Don't you think she's a diamond?'

Lucas nodded vigorously. 'I do. She's the best.'

'Catrin is the best, too,' Gareth said. 'She's too good for me.'

'You can say that again,' Ianto chortled. 'You were a prat to break up with her.'

'I want to spread my wings,' Gareth explained, solemnly. 'I want to live a bit before I settle down.'

'How are you going to do that?' Henry wanted to know. 'Are you going to play the field, or travel the world?'

'I'm going to have another drink.' Gareth finished his pint. 'Whose round is it?'

'Yours,' they chorused, and fell about laughing.

Lucas hadn't had this much fun in ages. It was simple, uncomplicated fun; although whether it was due to the amount of alcohol he'd imbibed or to the genuine connection he had with these guys, was difficult to tell. Why didn't he have mates like these in London?

'I love you guys,' he mumbled, throwing his arms around Gareth who was standing on one side of him, and Ianto, standing on the other. He didn't want Henry to feel left out, so he blew him a kiss.

'We love you, too, mate,' Henry said.

'I don't. I love Catrin.' Gareth was mournful.

'Don't tell us, tell *her*,' Ianto said.

'Can't.'

'Why not? If I loved a woman, I'd tell her,' Lucas said. Gracie's face swam into his head.

'Yeah, you gotta tell them, 'cause they like to hear stuff like that.' Henry burped. ''Scuse me. I love Lottie.'

'And I love Nora,' Ianto added.

'Good job, since you're going to be marrying her,' Lucas observed, feeling profound. He also felt rather inebriated. And unexpectedly happy.

'Told her I wanted a break,' Gareth said. 'I wasn't lying – I do want a break.'

'Sounds like you dunno what you want,' Ianto retorted.

'Yeah, I do – I want another pint. Whose round is it?' Gareth repeated, glancing around the group hopefully.

'We just told you – yours!'

'Oh, yeah, you did say. Anyone want another?'

Ianto slapped him on the back. 'Thought you'd never ask.'

–

'Show me the way to go home,' Gareth sang. 'I'm tired and I wanna go to bed. I had a little drink about an hour ago—'

'—and it's gone right to my head,' Lucas joined in. 'Flippin' heck, I haven't heard that for years. My grancha used to sing it whenever we went for a trip in the car.'

Lucas was propping Gareth up as they staggered along the street, heading for Gareth's house. Lucas was rather the worse for wear himself, but his newfound best buddy was even drunker, and he was worried the bloke mightn't get home without help.

Dimly Lucas wondered who would help *him* home after he'd helped Gareth. Oh dear, he really shouldn't have had that last pint. He'd been fine up until then.

'Here we go,' Lucas said, propping Gareth up against the door and wondering whether he should take the liberty of delving into the man's pockets for his keys, or whether he should ring the doorbell and pray Catrin would answer.

'Show me the way to go home...' Gareth launched into another rendition, louder than the last one as he slowly slid down the door.

A window rattled open, and someone yelled 'Shut up!' at the top of their voice before slamming it shut.

'Shhh,' Lucas hissed to Gareth.

'I'm tired an' I wanna go to bed...' This line was followed by an explosive hiccup.

Lucas's finger was poised over the doorbell, when the door abruptly opened.

He peered owlishly at the woman standing in front of him. 'You're not Catrin,' he stated accusingly.

'Oh, it's you.' Gracie's voice was flat. 'Give the man a gold star for observation.'

As she spoke, Gareth toppled backwards to land flat on his back half in and half out of the doorway. He grinned up at her. 'You're upside down,' he said.

'You're drunk,' she replied, staring down at him. 'And so are you.' She directed this last statement to Lucas.

'Only a bit,' he said. 'I'm not as bad as him. I haven't fallen over.' He was terrifically pleased that he'd managed to stay upright.

'Did you want a medal?'

'Have you got one?' Lucas would quite like a medal. He'd never been given one before.

'You'll have to pick him up; I can't lift him,' Gracie said, nudging Gareth with a pink-nailed toe.

Lucas held onto the wall as he bent down. 'You've got nice feet,' he observed.

'Please don't tell me you've got a foot fetish.' Her voice lacked warmth.

'OK, I won't tell you,' he agreed. She had nice ankles, too, and smooth legs. The legs stopped at the hem of a knee-length skirt. He hoped they went all the way to the top and didn't just end there, because that would be silly.

She didn't say anything, so he straightened up and met her horrified gaze.

'What?' he asked. 'Did you know your legs stop at your knees.'

'What on earth are you talking about? Just get him inside, before Catrin's neighbours complain.'

'That's OK,' Lucas hissed. 'They won't mind because they're Gareth's neighbours, too.'

'Oh, I think you'll find they will mind very much indeed.' Gracie turned her back on him and stalked into the house, leaving Lucas to hoist Gareth up and half-drag, half-carry the semi-comatose man inside.

'Where do you want him?' he asked, hesitating in the hallway as he saw Catrin sitting on the sofa. She didn't look particularly well either, and he wondered how much she'd had to drink as he noticed a wine bottle and a couple of glasses on a side table.

Catrin didn't look up. 'The spare room. You can stick him in there.'

To Lucas, she sounded as though she didn't care where he stuck Gareth.

'I'll show you,' Gracie said, and she led the way upstairs leaving him to struggle along behind her.

Damn and blast, this guy was heavy.

Panting, Lucas reached the landing and stopped for a breather. He debated leaving him right there, but he'd come this far, so he might as well take him into the bedroom. Catrin could see to him after that — there was no way Lucas was undressing him and putting him to bed.

'Love ya, mate,' Gareth muttered, as Lucas dumped him on the bed.

'That's good to know,' Lucas replied, the effort of heaving his new friend up a flight of stairs having sobered him up somewhat. He stood back. 'Catrin might want to bring him a bucket,' he suggested to Gracie.

'I'll tell her. You get off home. Thanks for bringing him back.' Her tone had mellowed slightly.

'You're welcome.' He sounded stiff and formal, but her attitude had cheesed him off. He hadn't known she was going to be here, had he? If he had, he might have urged one of the others to escort Gareth home, because she'd made it clear she didn't want anything to do with him.

'I'll see you Sunday,' she said, showing him out.

'Bye, Catrin,' he called from the hall, hoping he hadn't made too much of an idiot of himself.

She didn't answer so he guessed he must have.

'You don't have to come to lunch. Mum will understand if you're too busy.' He was giving Gracie a get-out-of-jail-free card.

She shrugged. 'I need you to try on your suit, so it might as well be Sunday.'

He felt like telling her that she needn't put herself out, but he thought it best to hold his tongue. After Sunday he'd make sure to keep out of her way, and it wasn't as though he had to spend the rest of his life with the risk of bumping into her.

He'd get through the next few weeks then he'd be gone, and if he hadn't already told his mother and Nora that he was staying in Applewell until after the wedding, he might very well have shot off back to London tomorrow – because being here in the same village as Gracie and not being able to be near her was doing his heart no good whatsoever.

Chapter 26

Gracie

When Gracie returned from showing Lucas out, Catrin looked up from the patch of carpet she'd been staring at for the past half hour, her expression stricken.

'What am I going to do?' her friend asked. 'Please can you take the wine away – the smell is making me feel sick.' A so-far unused bucket sat next to her feet. 'Is he OK?' She jerked her head towards the ceiling.

'I think so. He's fast asleep – or should I say he's passed out.' What a time to come home drunk! Gareth's timing was impeccable. Gracie wasn't too impressed with Lucas, either, although he'd not been as blotto.

He'd been the last person she'd expected to see this evening. It seems that hiding out in Catrin's house hadn't been the best idea – she might as well have gone to the pub. Except for one thing...

Gracie gathered up the barely touched bottle and the glasses, and emptied their contents into the sink in the kitchen before swilling the glasses out and leaving them on the draining board to dry.

'Can I get you anything?' she asked, walking back into the living room.

Catrin opened her hand. 'Not unless you've got an antidote to this.'

Gracie stared at the indicator her friend was holding and sighed. It clearly said 'pregnant'. There were no lines to confuse the issue – just that one word.

'They're not always a hundred per cent accurate,' she said for the second time since Catrin had taken the test.

'You don't believe that any more than I do.' Catrin barked out a bitter laugh. 'What a time to tell me he wants a break.'

'To be fair, he didn't know you were pregnant. You only found out this evening.'

Catrin had sent Gracie out for a test, too scared to go to the supermarket herself.

Luckily this request had come shortly after the wine had been opened but before Gracie had taken more than a sip. She hadn't had a chance, because Catrin had taken one sniff of the perfectly acceptable Pinot Grigio, had slapped a hand to her mouth and had dashed to the loo, where she'd thrown up noisily.

After the pair of them had discussed what Catrin had eaten for lunch (cheese and pickle sandwiches) and had mulled over last night's supper (a bowl of cereal because Catrin hadn't felt like cooking just for herself), they had circled around the only other obvious reason, once they'd ruled out food poisoning or a stomach bug.

'I can't be... you know...' Catrin had grimaced, but the two of them had stared at each other, their eyes wide as the truth slowly dawned. 'My period is due any day. My boobs are sore, I'm knackered, and I could cry at the drop of a hat.'

'When did you last have one?' Gracie had asked, thinking that those symptoms did sound remarkably similar to those of the early signs of pregnancy. But what did she know? She'd never been pregnant, and the way she was going she was unlikely to be in the foreseeable future. However, Catrin was clearly thinking the same thing.

'Um...?' Catrin thought. Her eyes had widened. She'd counted on her fingers. Then she'd checked the date on her phone. 'Seven weeks ago, give or take a couple of days.'

Gracie had said, 'You need to take a test, so you can rule out the possibility of you being pregnant.' But both of them knew it was the most likely explanation, given the evidence.

'Can you go and get one for me?'

Catrin had looked so worried that Gracie had instantly agreed and had driven to the nearest large out-of-town supermarket where there was less chance of her being seen, and had bought Catrin a test.

Catrin was now clutching the results in her hand as she had been doing for the past two hours.

Gracie thought her friend might be in shock.

It didn't help that Gareth was lying in the spare room, oblivious to what was going on in his own house. It should have been him sharing this moment with Catrin, not Gracie. Damn and blast the man.

'When are you going to tell him?' Gracie asked, pointing up at the ceiling.

'I'm not sure if I'm going to tell him at all. I wouldn't want to prevent him from *finding himself*,' she said, her tone bitter.

'He needs to know – whatever you decide, he has a right to be involved. He is the baby's father...'

'Oh God, there's a baby. I'm not just pregnant, I'm having a *baby*!'

Despite the gravity of the situation and her concern for her friend, Gracie couldn't help smiling. 'That's what being pregnant usually means.'

'I'm keeping it,' Catrin declared. 'I don't care what he says, I'm keeping it.' A look of wonder appeared on her face. 'I'm going to have a baby.'

'Yes, you are.' Gracie sat next to her, and this time when she put her arm around her it wasn't to offer consolation, it was to offer congratulations.

'My mother won't be happy,' Catrin said 'Not with Gareth buggering off around the world or whatever it is he intends to do in order to "spread his wings". I'm sure he thinks he's an eagle that's been kept in captivity and I'm the zookeeper; when in reality he's more like a tatty old cockerel – more noise than substance. He ought to thank me for putting up with him all these years, and not plucking him and boiling him up for broth.'

It was certainly an interesting and quite descriptive analogy. 'You don't mean that.'

Catrin had been in love with Gareth ever since Gracie could remember. Catrin did have a point about her mum, though. The woman wouldn't take kindly to Gareth getting her daughter pregnant, then not shouldering his responsibilities. If Gareth knew what was good for him, he'd better spread those wings of his soon, or he might find Catrin's mother clipping them for him permanently.

'Talking of Gareth, I'd better take him the bucket if you're not using it. And he's still wearing his shoes.'

'He can keep wearing them as far as I'm concerned. They'll be handy for when he wakes up and I tell him he's going to be a dad. It'll save him time before he runs away. Speaking of people running away, was that your Lucas who brought him home? I wasn't taking a great deal of notice.'

Now that the shock had worn off a little, Catrin was making some progress in returning to her normal self – or as normal as she'd been since Gareth had dropped his bombshell. It looked like Catrin was about to drop a bombshell of her own.

'He's not *my* Lucas. If anything, he's *yours*. You spend all day every day with him.'

'No, he's definitely yours,' Catrin said. 'He's actually a nice guy.'

Gracie thought he was too, and that was the problem. 'You're going to have to tell Gareth,' she repeated. It wasn't just an attempt on her part to change the subject. Gareth really did need to know.

'I don't want him to know.'

'He's going to have to, Cat.'

Catrin's eyes welled with tears. 'What if he decides to stay?'

'In Applewell?'

'With me.'

'That's good, isn't it?'

'Not if he's only staying because of the baby. I want him to stay because he wants *me*, not because he feels obliged to, or because he thinks it's the right thing to do.'

'You still have to tell him. It's his baby too, and he has the right to decide if he wants to be part of its life or not.'

'What if he doesn't?' Catrin turned pain-filled eyes to Gracie, and Gracie felt like crying for her. But she was determined to stay strong; if Gareth didn't want anything to do with his son or daughter, Catrin was going to need all of Gracie's help and support.

'I'm not going to be able to do this,' Catrin moaned. 'How can I raise a child on my own?'

'You won't be on your own. You'll have your mum, and me, and loads of other people. We'll all help you raise it.' Gracie honestly believed that – Catrin wouldn't be alone. There was a proverb that it takes a village to raise a child, and if that was true then there was no better village than Applewell. Catrin nodded. 'I know, but I'm scared.'

'I expect you are – I would be too.'

'Do you mind not saying anything to anyone just yet? I'm not going to tell anyone until the twelve-week mark.'

Gracie did a quick calculation. 'That's in about five weeks' time, maybe a week or so either side.'

Catrin wrapped her arms around her chest. 'Anyway, I want to keep it to myself for a bit, to have a chance to get used to it before the whole world knows. By then Gareth might have sorted himself out. Promise you won't tell anyone?'

'Not if you don't want me to.' Gracie got to her feet, wondering if she should offer to stay the night. 'Are you going to be OK?'

'I'm going to have to be, aren't I? I've got the baby to think of.'

As Gracie drove the extremely short distance home, her mind wasn't on Catrin, however – it was on Lucas's face when he had walked out of the door.

He looked so cold and distant that she knew she'd lost him. If, that is, she'd ever had him in the first place...

Chapter 27

Lucas

'I'm never drinking again.' Lucas had his head in his hands and was sitting at the kitchen table, bemoaning his stupidity. One pint had turned into more than he could count, and with having to get up this morning to go into UnderCover, he couldn't believe his loss of self-control. He was usually so good at knowing his limitations and abiding by them, but common sense had deserted him yesterday.

His mother had no sympathy for him whatsoever. 'Serves you right,' she said, banging a plate down on the table and making him wince. She bit into her toast with enthusiasm.

'Please could you crunch a little quieter?' he whispered.

'You should know better at your age.'

'Ianto was there; so were Henry and Gareth.'

'If one of those put their hand in a fire, would you shove yours in too?'

'It's not the same at all.'

'Just because they drank too much, doesn't mean you should. Grown men acting like teenagers.'

'We behaved ourselves,' Lucas protested.

'Not according to Nancy Felspar, who lives two doors up from Catrin. She said you were singing at the tops of your voices.'

'It's not eight o'clock yet – how do you know that?'

'Because she rang and told me.'

'It's like being a kid again,' he moaned. 'I can't do anything without someone snitching on me.'

Vivien stopped eating and put her toast down. 'Was it really that bad?'

He knew what she meant. 'Living in a village where everyone knows everyone else's business can be a little claustrophobic,' he said diplomatically.

His mother shrugged. 'It can also be comforting. Nancy rang me last night, not this morning. She suggested I leave a glass of water and some paracetamol next to your bed.'

'*You* did that? I assumed I'd done it myself before I went to bed. I was thinking I couldn't have been that drunk if I had the presence of mind to grab some painkillers.'

'You were three sheets to the wind, son. Although, to be fair, you were quiet enough when you came in.'

'What time was that?'

'Ten past eleven.'

God, it hadn't even been a late night. He must be getting old. 'Gracie was at Catrin's last night when I took Gareth home,' he said, straightening up.

'I bet Catrin wasn't pleased at the state he was in. I heard he was worse than you.'

'I don't think she noticed, and if she did, she was as drunk as he was. I remember seeing a bucket...' He also remembered the expression of disgust on Gracie's face, and his vow to avoid her from now on. Which wasn't going to be easy since she was coming to lunch tomorrow.

'Why don't you give the shop a miss today? Catrin is perfectly capable of managing without you.' His mother gave him a wry smile.

'It's an idea...' He didn't think he could face being jolly with customers today.

'I've got to go to work, otherwise I'd cook you a full breakfast,' Vivien said. 'I'm sure Eleri will oblige. You'll need something to soak up all that alcohol.'

'Ugh!' He didn't think he could face anything more substantial than coffee, and he wasn't even sure he could stomach that!

Wondering how the rest of his partners-in-crime were feeling, he had a shower, forced some water down his throat and went for a walk. He should really try to go for a run, but his head was pounding with each step he took, and he suspected it might fall off if he broke into a jog.

Fresh air and a fried breakfast should put him on the path to recovery, even if he didn't much feel like subjecting his body to either, so he took himself off to Eleri's cafe and prayed he wouldn't be sick in a hedge on the way.

'Take a seat,' Eleri said as soon as she saw him. 'I'll bring your breakfast over in a tick.'

'You don't know what I want.'

'I know what you need, and it'll start with strong hot coffee and end with a fry-up. You're getting the full works.'

Lucas groaned. He needed something in his stomach and a full English was a bit of a tradition as a hangover cure.

Whilst he waited for his meal to arrive, he phoned Under-Cover to let Catrin know he wouldn't be in.

'I gathered as much,' she replied.

'How is Gareth?'

'Don't know, don't care.'

Okaaay...

She added, 'He was conscious and complaining when I left, so I should imagine he's in the same state as you.'

'Tell him I said hi.'

'You might recall that we're not exactly speaking.'

Yeah, he knew that feeling, because Gracie wasn't speaking to him, either. A thought occurred to him. 'How come you haven't got a hangover? Or are you better at hiding it?'

'I didn't drink anything.'

That meant the bucket must have been for Gracie, although she'd seemed to be the soberest person in the house last night. He would never have guessed she was drunk.

'How is Gracie?' he asked.

'Ask her yourself,' Eleri said, popping a hot plate of fried food on the table in front of him and glancing meaningfully at the counter where Gracie was standing.

Hastily, he ended the call with Catrin and focused on Gracie; he had to admit she looked damned fine for a lady with a hangover. Her hair was pulled into a bun, although strands of it stuck out everywhere, her faced shone, her eyes sparkled, and she had a smile on her lips.

Her expression tightened when she saw him.

'Sit down and I'll bring it over,' Eleri said to her, pointing to the table he was sitting at.

Gracie shook her head. 'I only came in for a coffee – I can't stop. Saturday is one of my busiest days.'

'You can open at nine thirty,' Eleri told her. 'Have some breakfast first. Knowing you, you've only had cereal, or toast. What you need is a fry up. It'll help with your hangover.'

'I haven't got a hangover.' She frowned.

'Oh, I thought… Never mind. Sit yourself down anyway. Breakfast is on the house.'

Gracie took a step towards a free table.

'Not there – sit with Lucas. He looks like he could do with the company. Anyway, I don't want the pair of you taking up two tables when you can just take the one by sitting together.'

He watched Gracie narrow her eyes, and he thought she looked like a cat who was plotting revenge. Yet she did as she was asked, and as soon as she'd sat down, he joked, 'We must stop meeting like this.'

Gracie's reply was serious. 'Yes, we must.'

'Look, I don't know what I've done to annoy you, but whatever it is I didn't mean to do it and I'm sorry.'

Her lips twitched.

'OK, maybe I do know. I shouldn't have kissed you.' He gave a sly grin. 'I really enjoyed it though.' Then his expression became sombre. 'I'd be the same if I were in your shoes. I wouldn't want a casual affair, either.'

'You think I'm casual affair material, do you?'

'Not at all. I respect you too much for that.'

'Yeah, right.'

A phone rang, and it took him a moment to realise it was his. He pulled it out of his pocket and looked at the number. 'It's work,' he said. 'I'd better take it. Hi, Jonas, how are you?' He turned away and kept his voice low.

'Lucas, there's something I have to tell you before you hear it from anyone else – you remember that young chap with the tattooed head? You helped get him into a half-way house a couple of months ago?'

'Karl Traynor? I remember.' He recalled a lad in his early twenties who, on first meeting, had been suspicious and on edge, but who'd quickly revealed a dry and dark sense of humour. His stomach turned over as he guessed what Jonas was about to say.

'He died last night,' Jonas said.

'How?' Lucas reached for the table and gripped it with white-knuckled hands. Karl had sworn he was clean and Lucas had believed him.

'He was hit by a car.'

'Not drugs?'

'No, he liked a drink but as far as I know he didn't do drugs. The driver was an elderly woman who lost control. It was an accident, a tragic accident. Sorry, Lucas.'

'When's the funeral?' Lucas's throat constricted.

'I don't know yet; it's a police investigation so I doubt the body will be released for a while.'

'Does his family know?'

'Yeah, not that they give a damn. I'll let you know more when I can.'

'Thanks for telling me.' Lucas put his phone away, feeling shocked and desperately sorry for the young man who'd had so much life left to live. And just when he was getting on his feet, too.

'Do you want to talk about it?' Gracie asked, and his attention snapped back to her.

'You heard?'

'Enough to know that someone has died.'

Lucas told her about the young man he'd befriended. 'It's so unfair, so tragic. He'd had a dreadful start in life, and just when things were looking up for him...' He thumbed away a tear.

'I'm so sorry. Is there anything I can do?'

Lucas shook his head. 'Something like this makes you realise just how short life can be.'

'I think you knew that already.'

Her perception touched him. He felt her hand on his, and she gave it a squeeze.

'He reminded me of myself.' Lucas took a deep, deep breath, willing himself not to break down. 'Sorry, I don't think I can face breakfast.' He stood, took out his wallet and dropped some money on the table. 'Can you tell Eleri that something came up?'

'Of course. Take care, Lucas. I'm here if you need to talk.' Her eyes were large and full of sympathy and he knew her offer was genuine.

He felt the warmth of her concern as he walked out of the door, and he drew comfort from it for the rest of the day.

–

The waves were huge, crashing onto the beach in a plume of spray and running back like a torrent. Their rhythmical rage was oddly soothing in its predictability, white horses fleeing before the wind, cresting and dipping in the restless sea, driven by a low pressure over Ireland that was steadily moving Applewell's way. The village, which was at the edge of the west coast of Wales, was in for some rough weather overnight, but it should calm down tomorrow, according to the forecast.

Lucas was damp from the spray being carried high up the beach, but he didn't care; the wildness suited his mood. He felt like raging at the unfairness of a life cut so tragically short. Fury boiled inside him. He'd had enough heartache to last him a lifetime. Karl's was one death too many, and he hadn't even been all that close to the young man. Even though Lucas had done his best to help him, Karl had been as wary and as skittish as an untamed horse, but Lucas didn't care. Neither friendship nor gratitude had mattered to him – the only important thing was that Karl no longer lived on the streets.

Lucas's heart constricted with pain. Life, for some, was too damned short. He wondered what dreams the man had held, what hopes he'd had. And all for nothing.

What would Karl have done differently if he'd known his life was going to be snuffed out at twenty-two?

What would any of us do differently if we knew that death lurked around the next corner? Lucas wondered.

It was fruitless to think of what-if and if-only, because the past couldn't be changed. But the future could. Lucas had, until recently, thought his future would be in London. Even as he'd fled back to Applewell, he knew he'd return to the city.

It was a revelation to realise he didn't have to if he didn't want to. He could stay here, or move to another country. He could change jobs, change careers, make new friends. Find a new purpose – one that made him happy. His job was worthwhile, but it was starting to take a toll.

Thirty-four wasn't too old to start again. Heck, look at Henry Hargreaves! He'd changed careers and was now loving what he did.

The problem was, Lucas didn't know what else he could do. UnderCover was the only thing he was passionate about. However, something had to give.

He didn't want to go back to London and pick up the reins of his old life. He wanted to remain in Applewell with his family.

And, as he realised that this was where he wanted to be, he also understood that Gracie was who he wanted to be here with.

Chapter 28

Gracie

'I didn't think I'd ever see this,' Nora said on Sunday morning. She and Gracie were sitting side by side on a rock and gazing down the widening expanse of sand. The tide was going out and thankfully the weather was considerably calmer than it had been yesterday. Even though Applewell was two miles from the coast, the tang of wind-borne salt water had been strong, and Gracie could well imagine the waves pounding against the cliffs and onto the sand. The bank of driftwood behind them had definitely grown larger since the last time she was here.

Nora's eyes were on her daughter, her fiancé, and her brother, all of whom were crouching over a series of sandcastles. Ruby was directing the construction with bossy enthusiasm, and her two willing slaves were fetching water, digging moats and generally doing all the hard work.

'You and Lucas have a lot of time to make up for,' Gracie said, hoping she wasn't speaking out of turn.

'I hope it isn't a flash in the pan. I don't want Ruby to become attached to her uncle, only for him to disappear for another couple of years.'

'Has it been that long?'

Nora tucked a strand of flyaway hair behind her ear. 'It's been about a year since he was here last. And even then it was only for a couple of hours. I got the impression he hated it and couldn't wait to get back to London.'

'And now? He's been here nearly three weeks.'

'I don't know.' Nora's expression was guarded, and Gracie guessed that whatever the reason for Lucas being in Applewell for longer than a day, Nora didn't want to discuss it. If she actually knew, that is. Speculation had been rife in the village, but no one was nearer to discovering the truth. The rumours of him wanting to close down the UnderCover shop had finally subsided but, for want of an explanation from the horse's mouth, guesses ranging from being involved in gang warfare to hiding from an enraged husband had done the rounds.

Gracie suspected the truth was far less exotic.

'My brother seems to have taken a shine to you,' Nora said. 'I think he's lonely.'

'Do you?' Nora gazed at him, her head tilted slightly to the side. 'You might be right. Applewell is rather different from London.'

Gracie didn't say so, but she got the feeling he didn't have many friends in the city, either. Or much time to make any. She got the impression he was driven and single-minded, and that he lived for his work.

But maybe not as much now? The news about the young man who'd died seemed to have hit him hard yesterday, she thought. The glimpse she'd got of hidden depths beneath the good-looking exterior intrigued her. There were more facets to him than she had realised, and she would love to discover them, but it wasn't going to happen. He'd be gone and she'd be here, and never the twain shall meet again, so there was no point in starting something that would only have to end. Sooner rather than later in their case. Sometimes it happened later too, she thought, as Catrin and Gareth's crumbling relationship flitted across her mind. She'd assumed they were set for life, but look at them now – living separate lives even though they still shared a house. And now there was the added complication of Catrin being pregnant.

A flash of envy hit her in the stomach as Gracie thought of the baby.

Would *she* ever be a mother? Unlikely, considering she first had to find a man to fulfil one side of the equation, if she didn't want her baby's father to be a one-night stand or a passing fling. She wanted a proper relationship; she wanted to be loved and cherished, and to know that a baby would be a wonderful expression of their love for each other.

Look at Nora and Ianto. It was blatantly obvious how much they adored each other and their child.

Gracie wanted that, too, but she wasn't going to get it with a man who would be out of her life in just over a month. There was no point in starting anything, no matter how much she fancied him, nor how much he tugged at her heart.

One good thing had come out of being friends with Lucas though, and that was Nora. Gracie hadn't known the woman particularly well, even though there were only about three years between them, Nora being thirty-one to Gracie's twenty-eight. Gracie discovered she liked Lucas's sister immensely, and she hoped Nora felt the same way.

Nora was telling her all about the wedding and the honeymoon plans as the five of them made their way back to Vivien's house and lunch. The two men had hold of Ruby's hands, one either side of her, and were swinging her back and forth between them, much to the little girl's delight as squeals and shrieks filled the air.

'Have you lost any more weight?' Gracie asked as they entered the house and the delicious smell of roast lamb assaulted their noses.

Nora pulled a face. 'Not really, and I'm not going to if I keep eating my mother's cooking. I'm going to need panels put in my dress like you did for the christening gown Barbara's grandson was too big for.'

'Do you like my doll?' Ruby had raced ahead and was coming out of the living room to show her before Gracie had even hung her coat in the hall.

'I bought it in UnderCover,' Lucas said. 'There was quite a few of them but they're nearly all gone.'

Gracie must make some more; she had completed some already and if she put her mind to it, she could make another two or three this evening.

'It's lovely,' she said to Ruby, taking it from her for a moment to pretend to admire it, when what she was really doing was checking how well the stitching was holding up to being played with by a small child.

Satisfied it wasn't about to fall apart, she handed the doll back to Ruby when a thought struck her – what if she made the little girl a doll that looked like her? It would be easy enough to do.

Gracie loved it when lightbulb moments happened, and she had one right there; *she could take commissions*. Custom-made dolls could be a new arm to her business. What if she offered a doll-making service? People could send in photos of their children or grandchildren, or whoever they wanted the doll made for. She could even offer to use fabric that was special to the customer. It was a thought, and one she'd explore later when she was on her own.

'Do you want to see if the suit fits now, or wait until after lunch?' Lucas asked, jerking her into the present.

'Er, now, if that's OK,' she said, thinking that if she got it over with now, she wouldn't have to sit through lunch with the prospect of kneeling at Lucas's feet hanging over her.

She needn't have worried, however, because the alterations were perfect and she didn't have to get down on her knees to check the trouser hems.

'You scrub up well,' Nora teased her brother. 'I hope you're going to wear a shirt and tie for the wedding, because the way you look now with a T-shirt underneath that jacket, you only need to roll your sleeves up and you could be someone from a 1980's TV show.'

'Hey, you're the one who's going to be wearing a dress that's older than Mum,' he shot back. 'Don't diss my vintage suit.'

'I'm not sure it is vintage as such,' Gracie said. 'It looks good on you, though.' She bit her lip. Complimenting him wasn't part of keeping her distance and she blushed, aware that Nora was giving her a look. So was Vivien, who'd emerged from the kitchen to see her son in his suit.

Thankfully, the rest of the afternoon passed without incident, and when Gracie felt she could take her leave without being rude, she scuttled off, her tummy full of roast lamb with all the trimmings and rhubarb crumble with custard, and her mind full of Lucas.

On the way home she'd given herself a good talking to, and by the time she settled herself into her chair to sew, Lucas was hijacking only one thought in three. It was still too much, but it was the best she could manage, so she'd just have to put up with it.

–

Gracie hated being the centre of attention, but she had a Welsh dresser to pay for and a bargain to keep. Her heart was in her mouth and her lips were dry as she parked outside Lottie's workshop the following Tuesday evening. Conversely, her palms were clammy, and her back was damp with sweat.

She felt hot, bothered and incredibly nervous.

It didn't help that three students had already arrived and they gazed curiously at her as she walked into the workshop with her box of tools.

It also didn't help that upholstery was taking her out of her comfort zone, and she would have felt far more at ease if she had been asked to demonstrate how to line a jacket, or make a pair of dungarees. Or a five-tier wedding dress… Anything other than a chair, really.

The rest of the students filtered in, and as they did so, Gracie helped Lottie bring out a chair for each one of them and place them alongside the workbenches that were dotted around the room. At first Gracie assumed the students would be sitting on them, until she realised that every chair was similar to the one Henry had brought to the shop, and she understood that the students would be working on theirs at the same time as Gracie herself.

Feeling better about the situation (the thought of eight people staring at her for a couple of hours hadn't been nice), Gracie began to relax and take in her surroundings.

Lottie's workshop was adjacent to Henry's tip shop, which was next to the household waste reclamation centre itself. Henry's job was to salvage anything that was in good enough condition to be resold, whether it was a bed frame, a cooker, or a pram, and sell it in the tip shop. His wife salvaged a great many other things, and either repaired them or repurposed them, but she did so via running courses so that people learnt how to upcycle things for themselves. The whole idea was to reduce the amount of stuff going to landfill or having to be pulped or melted down. Lottie and Henry Hargreaves were a couple after Gracie's own heart, and she had nothing but admiration for them.

Still nervous at first, it didn't take long for Gracie to get into her stride and begin to enjoy herself. The students were a friendly bunch and threw themselves into their work with enthusiasm. The evening went surprisingly swiftly and before she knew it she was helping put the chairs away ready for next time.

'I'll come back and see the finished products,' she promised, as it would take the students at least one more session, if not two before all the chairs were completed.

'Thank you so much,' Lottie said as she saw Gracie out. 'Everyone had a great time, and they learnt a lot.'

'It was fun,' Gracie said; she was amazed that she'd enjoyed herself, although she wasn't sure whether she'd do it again.

Catrin phoned just as Gracie was parking her car and thinking about supper. She was starving and lunch felt like an awful long time ago.

'How did it go?' her friend asked.

'Good, I think. At least no one threw rotten tomatoes at me. More importantly, how are you?'

'I told Gareth this evening.'

'And?' Gracie was surprised; she'd thought Catrin wasn't going to tell him yet. She was pleased though – the man had a right to know.

'Can I pop over? I'll bring snacks.' Catrin's voice wasn't giving anything away and Gracie feared that his reaction hadn't been positive.

'In that case, you most certainly can.'

Gracie hurried inside, switched some lamps on, and filled the kettle. A situation like this would normally call for wine, but under the circumstances Gracie thought tea would be better.

'Well?' she demanded when Catrin knocked on the door and walked into the house a short while later.

Catrin was carrying a pizza box. 'Chicken with peppers and onion,' she said.

'Knickers to the pizza – what did Gareth say?'

Catrin turned a beaming face to her. 'He's delighted! And we're back together!'

Gracie squealed and did a little jig. 'That's marvellous news. I'm so pleased for you.'

'He said he'd been trying to pluck up the courage to admit he'd behaved like an arse.'

'What was all this talk about spreading his wings?'

'He said he likes the idea of being free, but when he got it he realised he didn't have a clue what to do with his freedom. Apparently, it wasn't what he thought it would be.'

'I thought he wanted to travel the world?'

'He thought he did, too. But when push came to shove, he couldn't face leaving his job. Or leaving me, which is why he hadn't moved out.' Catrin hugged herself. 'To be honest, I was tempted to tell him to shove off, and raise my baby on my own. But I love him, Gracie. I always have. Although we've only been apart for three weeks, they have been the longest three weeks of my life. I've been thoroughly miserable without him.'

'You don't say.' Gracie gave her a sly grin. 'Come here – let me give you a hug, then you can feed me pizza and give me a blow-by-blow account of exactly what was said.'

As they ate, Catrin described how she'd broken the news to him and his reaction. She looked so happy, Gracie's heart went out to her.

But there was a tinge of sadness to the joy she felt for her friend; Gracie also felt dejected – it seemed everyone was loved-up except her.

'What's wrong, hun?' Catrin asked after Gracie heaved yet another deep sigh.

She was about to say her usual 'nothing' when she decided to come clean. After all, Catrin had shared her problems with her, and wasn't that what friends were for? To share the bad times as well as the good? Gracie dearly wanted to confide in her and she knew Catrin would understand.

'It's Lucas. I've... um... fallen for him. But he'll be going back to London soon, so it's hopeless. *I'm* hopeless.' Why couldn't she have the hots for a local man instead? One who would stay put.

'Sweetie, don't be daft. You're not hopeless, just unlucky. You can't help who you fall in love with.'

'I'm not in love with him. But I could be, if I let myself.'

It was Catrin's turn to give her a hug and Gracie snuggled into it, feeling the warmth and compassion flooding from her friend's heart into hers.

'You'll find someone who's right for you one day,' Catrin said.

But that was the problem: Gracie suspected that Lucas *was* right for her. It was unfortunate that he lived so far away. Besides, she wasn't sure how he felt about her. She might believe he was right for her, but was *she* right for *him*?

As she prepared for bed later that evening, she thought how thrilled she was for Catrin. It was the best news ever. Catrin was such a lovely person, she deserved to be happy, and the baby deserved a father. Gracie wondered if Gareth would ask Catrin to marry him, and if he did would the wedding take place before or after the baby was born.

Gracie's thoughts turned to Nora and Ianto's wedding, and Lucas's suit and how good he looked in it. She could totally see him in a meeting with someone famous who had pots of money, like Tom Holland (she rather liked the Spiderman films) or the CEO of Unilever, and her heart ached to think that in a little over a month he'd be back in his own world and out of hers.

His life wasn't all glamour and meetings, she thought, as she recalled his devastated expression when he'd got the news of that young man's death. She could tell it had deeply affected him, and she'd been moved, despite not knowing the poor man. It was such a waste; he'd had his whole life ahead of him, and it sounded as though he was just getting back on his feet, too.

She felt total admiration for Lucas: by putting himself out there he risked being hurt, and he'd definitely been devastated by the news about Karl. It couldn't be easy for him, and if she had been in Lucas's shoes she wasn't sure she would be able to cope with it. She was too scared of being hurt to open herself up like that.

About to squeeze toothpaste onto her brush, Gracie paused. That was the problem, wasn't it? She was too scared of everything. She always had been. She couldn't blame it on her parents getting divorced (that had happened when she was twenty), neither could she blame it on her genes (both her mother and father were outgoing), or on her childhood (she'd had plenty of love and had done all the things kids usually did). However, it was always Gracie who'd hovered on the edge at parties, not keen on getting involved. It was always her who'd been the last to be picked to join the netball team, and if there was a game of tag in the playground she'd always preferred to sit on the sidelines and watch. Gracie had never put her hand up in class and had never volunteered for anything.

As she grew older, she found she didn't like going to the pub, or chatting to boys, or flirting. It made her uncomfortable, although she did periodically force herself to do all of those things (the flirting less so) and she'd had the occasional boyfriend. But she'd never felt truly happy unless she was sewing.

Her needlework was her inspiration and her shield, and she hid behind it as effectively as medieval peasants cowering behind a castle wall.

Gracie stared at her reflection in the mirror above the sink.

She looked the same today as she had done last week, last month, last year.

But she didn't feel the same inside.

Something had shifted; she couldn't put her finger on precisely what it was, but she could take an educated guess on the reason – Lucas.

Whether he'd meant to or not, he'd woken something inside her that she hadn't realised was asleep, and now all she could think about was him and how he made her feel.

Life was incredibly short, and she was a third of the way through hers, at a conservative estimate. And what did she have to show for it? No husband or partner, no children, few friends and no courage.

She was too scared of having her heart broken to allow herself to fall for Lucas any more than she already had.

But did she really want to hide behind her sewing and stay safe for the rest of her life, or did she want to grab life with both hands and live it to the full?

It was a question that was to keep Gracie awake for most of the night.

Chapter 29

Lucas

Four weeks seemed an age, but Lucas knew how quickly it would pass. He'd already been in Applewell for a month, and it seemed like only yesterday that he had driven down his mother's street and seen the banner she had put up for him.

He smiled, remembering how irritated he'd been. He'd also been surly and miserable, and the memory of how he'd acted wiped the smile off his face. It stayed off as he considered, for the umpteenth time, what he was going to do with himself.

It was all well and good deciding to stay in Applewell, he thought, as he delved into a carrier bag of donated goods and pulled out a squashed cowboy hat, but what was he going to live on? He could always continue to stay with his mum, but he'd still need a job. Besides, he didn't want to live with his mother for ever; he wanted his own place, and he'd only be able to afford that if he earned enough.

His flat in London had a hefty mortgage, so selling it would only net him enough for a deposit on a house in Applewell. The village might be a couple of miles from the coast, but house prices weren't cheap; there was the second-homers and the holiday rentals to thank for that.

A thought occurred to him — what if he rented his flat out? It might be an option…

Lucas stopped sorting donations for a moment and logged into his iPad to do a quick search. What he discovered made his jaw drop: London rental prices were astronomical. He knew they were high, but he didn't realise they were *that* high. Dear God, he could rent it out and use the income to pay his mortgage *plus* have enough left over each month to pay the rent on a property in Applewell. Ideally, he wanted to buy, but he didn't have any money for a deposit, unless he sold his flat.

What should he do for the best?

He wished there was someone he could discuss this with, to bat ideas around with and who would give him impartial advice. His mum was out of the question, as was Nora, and he certainly didn't want to discuss it with Jonas. None of them could be objective, and he didn't want to upset the applecart when it came to Jonas until he was utterly certain of his decision and his next course of action.

Gracie's face came into his mind, but if he spoke to her about it, then he was the one who was at risk of becoming emotional and letting his heart rule his head, because the thought of seeing her every day was one of the most appealing things about staying in Applewell.

How about Ianto? Or Gareth?

He exhaled the breath he realised he was holding and went back to work. Nice sandals, he thought, checking them carefully to make sure the straps were intact. Satisfied, he put them on the saleable pile.

'Chanel,' he murmured, looking at the label on the knitted dress he'd just lifted out of the bag.

It was short with capped sleeves, and was in an oatmeal colour. Surely it was a fake? He thought Chanel only made bags and little black dresses.

'What do you make of this?' he called to Catrin, who'd been looking so much happier this past week. She still appeared to be tired, but her whole demeanour was lighter, and he'd occasionally caught her with a dreamy expression on her face. He hoped it was because she and Gareth had made up, but he didn't like to poke his nose in and ask.

'What have you got there?' Catrin sauntered over with a duster in her hand. She'd been cleaning the china and ornament shelves, not trusting him to do it after he'd knocked over and broken a vase last week.

Lucas held the dress up.

'It's lovely and all, but I don't think it would fit you. It's not your colour, either.' She giggled. 'If you want my opinion, your hairy legs sticking out of the bottom of it would not look good.'

'Leave my legs alone,' he retorted. 'They're not that hairy.'

'I'll take your word for it.'

'It says Chanel on the label,' he said, shaking the dress at her. 'Look.'

Catrin looked. 'So it does.' She raised her eyebrows. 'Do you think it's genuine?'

'I don't know. I was hoping you might.'

'No idea,' she replied cheerfully.

'Is it possible to find out?'

'Google it,' she suggested. 'I'd be surprised if it was.'

'Me, too. But just in case.' He wondered what it would be worth if it was genuine. A hundred pounds? Two hundred?

He picked up his iPad again and typed in 'how to tell if a Chanel dress is genuine' and studied the results.

'Hmm...' he murmured, checking the label. It looked real: the font looked the same as the examples he'd found online, as did the season and composition tag. The garment had been made in France, which was what he'd expect to see based on the information he was reading.

'Do you know, I think it *is* genuine,' he declared, holding it with considerably more care than when he'd pulled it out of the carrier bag.

The site he was on advised him to type the reference code into a search engine to find details of the piece.

'Crumbs,' he said. 'It *is* genuine.' He showed Catrin what he'd discovered, and she was as shocked as he when she saw how much various sites were selling the same dress for.

'Well, I never!' she declared. 'You do realise that we'll never get anywhere near that for it.'

'Yes, that's what concerns me.'

'If you put it for sale in one of the London branches, would you get a decent price?' she asked.

'I'll have to look into it,' he replied.

Lucas had no idea, though his guess was probably not. He really should discuss this find with Jonas. Then there was the conversation he'd had with Gracie a while back about selling designer stuff online, rather than through the UnderCover shops where the charity would only receive a fraction of what they would if the item was sold on eBay, for instance. Would it be easier to use a platform like that to sell the clothes and accessories, or would it be better to use the charity's existing website, or even set up a new one? All these things had to be considered, and he didn't know where to start. He could just dump the whole thing in Jonas's lap and let him look into it, but Lucas had a gut feeling that this idea of his could lead to something big, and he wanted to present as thorough a business case as possible to Jonas.

'Gracie might have an idea,' Catrin said. 'She's heavily into vintage stuff and she loves old clothes.'

'I was under the impression she recycled fabric and made stuff out of bits and pieces. Does she do other things as well?' He thought of the red coat and a shiver of unease ran through him. Maybe Gracie wasn't the best person to ask, after all.

'She does alterations – lots of them. For brides and prom dresses mainly, but she'll sew anything you ask her to. She doesn't sell clothes, though.'

'Not even ones that only need a bit of a mend?'

'No, but I suppose she could do. She's got a website where she sells the things she makes, which used to be her main source of income until she opened the shop, but it wouldn't be any good for clothes. She'd be better off using eBay or Vinted for that.'

'Is that what she does? Sell on eBay?'

'I don't think so. What else is in that bag? Give it here, there might be some other tasty stuff.'

'Tasty stuff?'

'Yeah, designer. Ooh, look, a cowboy hat.' Catrin made a grab for it and plonked it on her head. 'How do I look?'

Lucas smiled. 'Ridiculous.'

'Thanks.' She removed it and gave it back to him. 'It'll do for fancy dress,' she said. 'Maybe I'll buy it in case Gareth and I get asked to any fancy dress parties – he could go as a cowboy and I could go as Hiawatha. I can see myself in a pair of moccasins, with a feather in my hair.'

'You and Gareth? Does that mean…?'

Catrin beamed. 'It does. We're back together.'

'I'm so pleased. When I brought him home the other Friday, he was saying how much he loves you.'

'He was?' Her beam grew even wider. 'He definitely said that?'

'He did.' Catrin was glowing, and Lucas was delighted that she was so happy. 'How long have you two been together?'

'Ten years. We were sweethearts in school.'

'Wow!'

'How about you? Have you got anyone special?'

Gracie, he almost said. 'No, no one.'

'You're older than Nora, aren't you?'

'Are you suggesting that I'm knocking on a bit and need to settle down?'

Catrin laughed. 'If the cap fits…'

'Cheeky. Talking about settling down, Nora is turning into a right diva. She's driving my mum to distraction. Fraught is the best way to describe her.'

'She's being a bridezilla, is she?'

'A what?'

'That's the term used to describe ultra-demanding brides.'

'She's one of those, all right – all she can talk about is the wedding. Thank God Ianto is more laid back. We went out for a drink the other night, and he didn't mention the wedding once.'

'It's nice that the two of you get on.'

'I like him,' Lucas said, simply. 'Nora's got a good bloke.'

'It's a pity you're leaving, but at least you'll have someone to go out for a drink with when you come home. You *will* be coming back to Applewell, won't you?'

Lucas hesitated, torn between reluctance to share the news that he wasn't going to return to London because he needed to tell his family and Lucas first, and not wanting to lie.

Catrin heaved a sigh. 'It's probably for the best if you don't,' she said, when he didn't answer her.

'You think it's better if I don't visit Applewell? Better for whom?' he wanted to know.

'Oh, damn, I shouldn't have said anything.'

'You can't leave it there,' Lucas protested. 'Why shouldn't I come back?' He was confused and a little hurt to think that he wasn't welcome, and he wondered who it was who felt that way. Nora? His mother? Surely not.

'Gracie, but don't you dare say anything to anyone.' Catrin's expression was worried.

'Gracie? I don't understand. Why would Gracie not want me to come back to Applewell?'

'She likes you. A lot.' Catrin said, but Lucas still didn't understand. Catrin sighed. 'You're leaving. There's no hope of any relationship between the two of you. To be honest, I'd feel the same.'

'Gracie likes me?' Oh, wow...

Lucas allowed himself a secret smile. That particular piece of information was the best thing he'd heard in a long time.

Chapter 30

Gracie

Gracie blinked and swallowed nervously when the door to her shop opened and Lucas sauntered in, with a smile on his face and a twinkle in his eye. She'd not seen him since last Sunday and to say that she was surprised to see him today was an understatement.

'Hi,' she said warily, wondering what he wanted.

'Can I pick your brains?'

Gracie giggled nervously. 'If you can find any to pick,' she quipped, then she bit her lip at her audacity. She'd never been a flirter, but she seemed to be doing her best to flirt with Lucas whenever she saw him, even though that wasn't her intention.

'How about I take you out to dinner, and we can have a chat then?' he suggested.

Gosh, she hadn't been expecting that. Her first panicked thought was to wonder what she was going to wear, closely followed by *oh my God, he's taking me out to dinner.* She hesitated.

'That's if you want to,' Lucas said. 'You can always say no.'

'No, I mean yes. Yes, please.'

'Are you just saying that because you want someone else to do the cooking?' His smile was teasing.

'You know me too well.' Oh dear, there she goes again, more flirting.

'I don't think I do, but I would like to get to know you better.'

'Would you?' She sounded breathless and she knew she was blushing. She was practically fluttering her eyelashes and simpering. Cross at her reaction to him, she scowled.

'Sorry, I didn't mean to annoy you.'

'Pardon?'

'You frowned when I said I'd like to get to know you better.'

'I didn't mean to. Shall we start again?' She took a steadying breath. 'Yes, please, I'd like to go to dinner with you. You can pick my brains all you want in exchange for a three-course meal.'

'You're bartering again, aren't you?'

'I like bartering.'

'Who said anything about three courses?'

'That's my minimum fee.'

'What do I get if I throw in some wine?'

'I expect wine, anyway. You can't have dinner without wine. What do you want to pick my brains about?'

'Shall we leave it until dinner? Is tonight OK for you, or do you have other plans?'

Gracie thought of the plans she'd made, which consisted of a piece of toast when she got home, possibly with some jam on it, along with a cup of tea, some mindless TV, and her beloved sewing. All of which she'd quite happily pass up in exchange for dinner. Especially dinner with Lucas. 'No plans,' she confirmed.

'I'll drive,' he said. 'Shall I pick you up at seven thirty?'

She'd assumed they were going to The Busy Bumble so was disconcerted to hear they were to drive. 'Seven thirty is fine. Where are we going? I'm only asking so I know what to wear.'

'There's a Thai restaurant in Aberystwyth; would that be OK?'

Gosh, she thought, that would be nice. She loved Thai food, not that she got to eat it very often. Applewell wasn't really known for its Thai cuisine. 'Lovely,' she said. 'I'll see you later.'

She hoped she sounded serene and calm, but inside her stomach was performing a somersault, and in her head she was jumping up and down and shouting 'Squee!'

Of course, the first thing she did was to ring Catrin. 'You'll never guess who's asked me to dinner,' she squeaked down the phone. 'Lucas!' she exclaimed.

Catrin's voice was quiet. 'Yes, I know; he's just come back in.'

'What is all this about?' Gracie found herself whispering too, then she cleared her throat as she realised how ridiculous she was being; he couldn't possibly hear her side of the conversation.

'I can't talk,' Catrin whispered.

'Send me a text. I need to be prepared.'

'You don't, honestly you don't. I think it's just an excuse to have dinner with you.'

'What is?'

'Don't worry about it, just enjoy yourself.'

'How can I? I've got nothing to wear. He wants to take me to a Thai restaurant in Aberystwyth.'

'Lucky you, I hear it's really good. Expensive, too.'

That piece of news didn't make Gracie feel any better.

Catrin said, 'Don't worry about not having anything to wear. Come to mine straight from work and you can see if you want to borrow something.'

'I'm curvier than you,' Gracie pointed out, then held the phone away from her ear when Catrin burst out laughing.

'No, you're not,' Catrin said. 'Whatever gave you that idea? If anything, my clothes are likely to be too big on you.'

'Are you sure?'

'I'll see you later. And Gracie…?'

'Yes?'

'Try not to fret. You're going to have a great time, I know it.'

'I'm not sure whether I *should* be having a great time,' Gracie said. 'After all, this isn't a date. He wants to pick my brains, in exchange for dinner.'

Catrin laughed so hard she hung up on her, and Gracie was left holding a dead phone and wondering what was so funny.

'Do I look all right?' Gracie asked her reflection, as she twisted from side to side. She was probably as ready as she'd ever be for her dinner with Lucas. He was due to pick her up in a few minutes and she was panicking about whether she'd do.

Catrin had given her some serum to rub through her hair to tame it a little. Her friend had been trying to get her to use it for years, saying that it would do wonders for controlling her curls, but Gracie hadn't been keen. She'd tried straightening it once, with unfortunate results, and so had been wary of using anything ever since. But she thought she'd give the serum a go this evening, with the proviso that she could always quickly wash it out again if it was disastrous.

To her amazement, it actually made her hair look glossy. Each corkscrew curl was defined, and the frizz had gone. Crikey, she really must get some of this stuff for herself. It had taken a bit of effort, but perhaps it was worth it.

She never wore foundation and she didn't this evening. Covering her freckles was impossible unless she used tons of foundation, but that clogged up her skin and made her look as if she was wearing a mask. Instead, Catrin had given her some mascara because the one Gracie owned had dried up, and that was the only make-up she wore now; just a swipe of it across her lashes.

That wasn't all Catrin had given her. Gracie was wearing the most gorgeous deep navy dress: strappy, elasticated at the waist, with a flowing skirt and tiny white flowers to break up the navy.

She didn't recognise herself, and she couldn't remember ever looking so feminine. She teamed the dress with ballet pumps that she already owned and a soft leather clutch bag, and she hoped she looked OK.

She was waiting downstairs when she saw Lucas's car pull up. Careful not to touch the curtain in case he noticed that she'd been peering through the window, she dashed to the front door, grabbed her keys and slipped outside. She hadn't expected him to get out of his car to hold the door open for her, but that was exactly what he was doing.

Oh lordy, this wasn't just a simple pick-your-brains session in exchange for food. This was a date. Not a business transaction.

She kind of knew it was, otherwise why would she have dressed up? She had tried to tell herself it was because she was going to a posh restaurant and that she didn't want to let the side down, but deep down she'd known the truth of it. Date. Not business. Not even friends. *Date.*

She smiled shyly at him as she slipped into the seat and arranged her dress around her legs. He clicked the door shut and got into the driver's side.

'You look lovely,' he said.

As did he. He was wearing a pair of simple black jeans and a grey shirt which had a very slight sheen to it. He looked sexy and casual, and far too confident and good-looking to have her on his arm. She wondered if she'd read the situation wrong, and that he opened car doors for everyone he gave a lift to.

Unused to being given compliments, all Gracie said was, 'Thank you.'

It was a nice change to be driven. Whenever Gracie wanted to go somewhere she always drove herself. Not that she went very far, just to the big supermarket every couple of weeks, but rarely did she go any further afield than that, except for occasionally going to somebody's house for a bridal fitting. Sometimes she wondered why she had a car at all, because she hardly ever went out in it. It wouldn't occur to her to drive to Aberystwyth, for instance: not on her own. And although she and Catrin were very good friends, they didn't usually do days out. Catrin had Gareth, and Gracie fully understood. She would be the same if there was someone special in her life.

Lucas drove effortlessly, negotiating the roads between Applewell and Aberystwyth with ease, keeping up a casual conversation about nothing much. If it had been Gracie driving, she'd be gripping the wheel with both hands, her knuckles white, her eyes staring rigidly ahead. She was feeling as relaxed as she could possibly feel considering she was on a date (*was* it a date?) with a man she was falling for and wondering if she was dressed appropriately.

Her attire was perfectly fine she saw with relief, when he escorted her into the restaurant, opening doors for her after confirming his booking with one of the servers. She didn't look out of place at all, she thought, as she followed the server to the table.

Lucas pulled out a chair for her and she sat down, feeling very self-conscious and wondering if everyone was staring at her. When she glanced around, no one was taking the slightest bit of notice.

'Did you want white or red wine?' Lucas asked, and she jerked back to him, her eyes wide.

'Wine?'

'That was part of the deal, remember?' His eyes sparkled, and he twinkled at her.

'Will you be having any?' she asked.

'Not when I'm driving.'

'Then I won't have any, either,' she said.

'Please don't let me stop you. I'm quite happy to order a bottle or a glass, whichever you prefer.'

Gracie was sorely tempted to drink a whole bottle, just to have some Dutch courage, but she was also very aware that she could make a total and utter fool of herself if she had too much to drink, so she said, 'I'll just have a sparkling water, please.'

'Make that two,' Lucas said to their server.

Gracie, her eyes on the menu, asked, 'You said you wanted to pick my brains?'

'We can do it later.'

'No, I'd like to fulfil my end of the bargain now.'

'OK, but afterwards promise me you'll let your hair down a bit.' He reached across the table and took hold of a strand of hair in his fingers, straightening it out and then letting it go. It bounced against her cheek. 'Have I told you that you look beautiful?'

Gracie felt like a rabbit caught in headlights. 'Yes, I think you did,' she squeaked.

'It's true, you do.'

'Brains?'

'I don't think brains are on the menu,' he shot back at her with a smile.

No, but I am, she thought, then gasped.

'Is everything all right?' he asked.

'Yes, I, um, kicked the chair leg. Stubbed my toe.'

'Do you want me to rub it better?' He closed his eyes slowly and shook his head. 'That came out wrong,' he said opening them again and giving her a worried look.

Gracie had a sudden vision of his hands on her feet, and unaccustomed heat swept through her.

Of course she was blushing again. She was probably going to spend the whole evening blushing.

'Brains,' she reminded him firmly.

'We had a genuine Chanel dress come into UnderCover today,' he began. 'I don't think we should sell it in the shop.'

'Goodness, no! You'd get hardly anything for it. People don't usually go into charity shops, especially in a small place like Applewell, and expect to pay a couple of hundred pounds for something. Even if it *is* worth a considerable amount of money, they will still expect to buy it for next to nothing.'

'I'm not sure we'd get a great deal more for it in London,' he said. 'I'd have to speak to Jonas about that. But something you said a while back made me think it might be a good idea to try to sell it through a third party like eBay, or sell it directly to people through the charity's website. What do you think?'

'I think it's a brilliant idea; eBay is the logical choice, because thousands and thousands of people look on there every week.

In fact, it would be the easiest thing to do. You could either use the auction option, or you could use the buy-it-now option.'

'Do you sell much on eBay?'

'No. I used to, but then I went to Etsy.'

'I've never heard of that. What is it?'

'It's an online marketplace that specialises in handmade things. You can find all kinds of rather wonderful handcrafted items on there. I use it sometimes, but I've also got my own website, and I mostly sell through that.'

'A dedicated website is something I was considering. Not me actually, because it wouldn't be my decision, but I wanted to present all the options to Jonas so he has enough information at his fingertips to be able to take it further.'

'It will take quite a lot of work, whichever way you cut it,' Gracie said, thinking aloud. 'There's the issue of listing things for a start; whether you do it on a third-party site or on your own website you've still got to take photographs, come up with the description, set a price. And when it's sold, it has to be packaged up and posted off. Whichever platform you use to sell the goods, somebody would have to be on hand to answer questions – because believe me, people do ask questions – or to respond to offers. It could start off as a one-person job but, depending on how successful you are, you might end up having to take on more staff.' She frowned and rephrased it. 'Sorry, I meant have more volunteers. Although you might want to pay someone to oversee the whole thing. Besides, where would you do this from? You can't have each shop doing their own thing and listing their own stuff, because you'd want some consistency. You might be able to manage it for eBay, but how many people would have access to the charity's eBay account? The same applies to a website.' She took a breath and Lucas held up his hand.

'Whoa, stop there,' he laughed. 'See, this is why I needed to talk to you. I don't really know how these things work. I'm not sure that Jonas would know either. You've certainly given me a lot to think about.'

'I can come up with plenty more.' Gracie was just hitting her stride, as thoughts flitted through her head like items on a conveyor belt.

'That's enough to be going on with, thank you,' he said. 'You've earned your dinner. Have you decided what you'd like to have?'

Gracie hadn't looked at the menu properly. She took a moment to decide then sat back, sipping her water and wondering what else they could talk about, now that he'd picked her brains.

She needn't have fretted. Lucas guided the conversation, asking her questions, and even though Gracie wasn't too keen on preparing and cooking it, she was very good at eating it, and she tended to like most things so they discussed their food preferences for a while. Then Lucas regaled her with stories of how hopeless he had been at cooking in the beginning, and how he had once tried to cook a whole chicken in a frying pan, and how he'd put too much milk in the mashed potato and it had ended up more like potato soup.

They were drinking coffee by the time the conversation slowed down, and she was happy to just sit back and sip her drink, and not feel obliged to talk. It was a comfortable silence, one that she had never experienced with a man before. With Lucas she didn't feel the need to chat constantly. He made the occasional comment, and so did she, but there was no urge to keep talking, and the comfortable silence continued as he drove her back to Applewell.

But the nearer they got to the village, the more nervous she began to feel.

Would he want to come in for coffee? Should she invite him in? If she did, would he expect more than coffee? Would *she* want more than coffee?

Oh dear, that was really silly; of course she wanted more than coffee. She wanted kisses, lots and lots of them. She wanted something else too, but her mind refused to take her there. She couldn't envisage any man in her bed, let alone *this* man, who she wanted more than she'd ever wanted anyone else. Kisses she could do; she knew what he tasted like, how it felt to have his arms around her. But as for anything more, she didn't know whether she was ready.

The question was, what would happen if she decided not to take it any further and rebuffed his advances – assuming he made any? He mightn't: this evening might have been purely a business transaction. But deep down she knew it hadn't been. She'd had a wonderful time with a wonderful man, and she didn't want the evening to end. But if it didn't end when he drew up outside her house, it meant she was inviting him in, and not just for a nightcap. She'd be letting him into her heart as well as into her bed.

Was she ready for that, knowing that she'd lose him all too soon?

The memory of that poor young man who had tragically died flitted across her mind. He would never have the opportunity to debate the wisdom of falling in love – which was exactly what was happening to her. She didn't know anything about him apart from his name, but she had the feeling he would tell her to seize love with both hands. Because loving someone, however fleetingly, was better than not loving at all.

Would she regret loving Lucas?

Yes – because her heart would break when he left.

But would she regret *not* loving him, more?

Undoubtedly – because she hadn't known she could feel like this, and feeling something, however painful it might turn out to be, was infinitely better than never feeling anything at all.

Gracie waited until Lucas had accompanied her to her front door, his car keys still in his hand.

'I enjoyed myself tonight,' he said. 'Can I see you again?'

Her heart thudded erratically, and she took a shaky breath. 'I'd like that.'

He nodded once and turned slightly, about to leave, and Gracie made a decision. Catching hold of his sleeve, she stepped closer to him, and kissed him.

It was the bravest and most daring thing she'd ever done.

Chapter 31

Lucas

Walking away from Gracie had been the hardest thing Lucas had ever done. He wanted her so badly it hurt, but he didn't want to rush her and he didn't want her to do anything she'd regret. Therefore, he did the only thing he could do – he kissed her soundly, matching her passion, then he drew back slowly, the heated kisses turning to gentle nibbling and eventually to a fluttered meeting of the lips. A final kiss on the nose and a trail of his fingers down her cheek, and he pulled away.

'Can I see you tomorrow?' he asked, letting her know that this wasn't the end of anything, but the start.

'If you like.'

'How about lunch? I can meet you in Eleri's cafe. I can't wait until the evening.'

Her pupils were huge, and there were depths to them he longed to fathom. She licked her lips, and his attention was drawn to their swollen pinkness. He caught his bottom lip between his teeth – their embrace had been long and passionate, and he hoped he hadn't kissed her too hard and bruised her. But her mouth was so irresistible that he ached to do it again.

'I'll be there at two o'clock,' she said. 'You realise people will talk?'

'Does that bother you?'

She shook her head.

'I promise not to kiss you – not in public anyway.' He crossed his heart.

Gracie giggled, the sound tinkling along his veins. 'I think it's public enough right here,' she said, shooting glances at the surrounding houses.

Lucas noticed a net curtain twitch. 'Would you prefer to go somewhere other than the cafe?'

'Aside from The Busy Bumble, there is nowhere else. I can't go too far because of the shop.'

'Then lunch shall come to you,' he told her. 'We can eat in the shop, and I can kiss you afterwards.'

Her blush gave him butterflies.

He didn't know how he managed to get back in his car and drive home, but he did, thinking of her and nothing but her, and he had a feeling it was going to be this way for a very long time indeed.

—

Sleep had been a long time coming, and when it had arrived it had been fitful and restless. Lucas hadn't been able to settle: he'd been too wound up and too excited, his mind churning with possibilities. First and foremost there was Gracie, swiftly followed by the designer goods project, and when he wasn't thinking about either of those things, he was worrying about finding a job and somewhere to live.

The next morning saw him up with the lark and on the phone to Jonas almost before a decent time.

'You're early,' Jonas said, as he answered the phone. 'Is something wrong?'

Lucas could hear the sounds of dishes and cutlery, and he guessed Jonas was still at home enjoying breakfast with his family. 'Just the opposite. I've got an idea.'

'Go on.' Jonas sounded cautious.

'A genuine Chanel dress came into the shop in Applewell yesterday,' Lucas began. 'I'm not quite sure what to do with it. Do you know what normally happens to these kinds of donations?' Lucas had been thinking about his idea most of the night, and he was ready to type it up and email it across to Jonas, but first of all he wanted to check that this wasn't something that had already been considered or tried.

'As far as I know they are priced up as normal and sold in the shop they were donated to,' Jonas said. 'Why? Do you want me to look into it?'

'I think it might be an idea,' Lucas said. He cleared his throat. 'Do we know how many of these high value items are donated?'

'I don't see how we could. There isn't a central collection point: people just drop things off at their nearest charity shop, so we've no idea what comes in.'

'That's what I was worried about. I know the shops charge a premium for certain named brands, but what happens to the high-end items?' He went on to outline his thoughts, alongside all the benefits and the pitfalls, ending up with, 'Is that something you would be interested in looking into?'

'Most certainly.'

'OK, I'll write it up and email it off to you. At least it will give you a starting point.'

'I'm glad to see the break is doing you good,' Jonas said. 'I was starting to get a little worried.'

'To be honest, so was I.'

'When is your sister's wedding?'

'In four weeks.'

'Do you think you'll be ready to return to work in a month? I hope you will; you're sorely missed. Angel Beddows has been taking over some of your work and she's doing a fine job, but she's not as good at it as you are.'

'I'm sure she will be with practice,' Lucas said, feeling a degree of relief at the thought that someone was stepping into his shoes. Angel was more than capable; she just needed to develop the right contacts. He bet she was loving the challenge. He'd loved it once, but not anymore.

Lucas was serious about not going back to London, and he had an awful lot to sort out in a very short space of time. He didn't want to leave Jonas in the lurch, but with Angel taking over from him, Lucas was happy to know that his branch of fund raising would be in capable hands. According to his contract, he only had to give a month's notice, and he really should be doing that now, but he wasn't quite ready yet.

It was a big step and he wanted to make sure he was doing it for the right reasons. Of course, as he'd previously thought, being closer to his family was important, and even more so now that he'd reconnected with them. He was just getting to know Nora all over again and marvelling at the wonderful woman she'd turned into. Then there was his growing friendship with Ianto, and he was pretty certain he could find firm friends in both Gareth and Henry. There was also Ruby, his cute little niece. He loved spending time with her, and the thought of not seeing her for months on end made his heart sore. Neither could he forget his mother, who was thrilled to have him home, and who would be even more thrilled to have him live close by. They were getting along together quite nicely, even though he'd been used to his own company for so many years, and his mother had lived alone since Nora had moved out. It should have been a recipe for disaster, but it wasn't.

Last but not least – most definitely not least – was Gracie.

Was she the main reason he wanted to remain in Applewell? If so, it was a worry. He didn't want to base such a major decision on a barely-begun romance. Their relationship had only just started, and who could say whether it would work out? How would he feel if he gave up everything in London for Gracie, only to discover that they weren't right for each other? Would he regret the decision? Would he want to go back to the city and his former life?

No, he concluded, he wouldn't. Even taking Gracie out of the equation, he realised he hadn't been as happy as this in a very long time. The discontent had been gradual, creeping up on him so slowly that he hadn't noticed it until the pain of Effron's death had shifted it rudely to the forefront of his mind and made him take stock.

He didn't want to return to that world; he wanted to stay here where his roots were. He felt at home, both physically and emotionally. This is where he belonged, either with or without Gracie. Preferably with.

Most definitely with.

Lucas wanted Gracie to be the most significant person in this new life of his; he was falling for her more and more each time they met, and very soon he would have fallen so far he'd never be able to climb back out again.

The thought of being in love with Gracie was a heady one.

All he hoped was that she felt the same way about him and, to ensure she did, he was going to woo her with everything he had – heart, mind, and body.

Chapter 32

Gracie

'Happy birthday to you, happy birthday to you, happy birthday, dear Gracie, happy birthday to you!' Lucas sang, then whipped out a bunch of flowers from behind his back and presented them to Gracie who beamed at him and accepted them graciously.

Lucas buying her flowers was becoming a regular occurrence. The past two weeks had seen him buying her flowers every few days, or presenting her with other tokens of his affection, including chocolates, a pretty fragrant soap he'd found in one of the gift shops, a bucket and spade in case she wanted to help him build sandcastles on the beach, which she did, competing with Ruby but obviously letting the little girl win.

Gracie and Lucas had spent almost every spare waking hour since that wonderful meal in the Thai restaurant in Aberystwyth with each other. In fact, Gracie was beginning to resent the amount of time she had to spend in her shop because she wanted to be with Lucas. It didn't help that his hours were more fluid, Lucas having been instructed by Jonas to do some proper groundwork for the new designer outlet. She enjoyed chatting to Lucas about it, letting him bounce ideas off her while she played devil's advocate, until gradually a working model had been developed, and he was very close to presenting it to the board.

She didn't mind talking about the project, but she didn't want to think too closely about the fact that Nora's wedding was in two short weeks. After that, Lucas would be two hundred and fifty miles and a whole world away from her. She kept pushing it to the back of her mind, not prepared to think about it.

She didn't even want to consider how their relationship would carry on, because she knew it couldn't. He'd live there, she'd live here, and that would be the end of it.

'Are the flowers OK?' Lucas asked, and when she heard the concern in his voice she forced herself to brighten up.

'They're lovely.' She reached up to kiss him.

The world faded for a moment, until Lucas withdrew, saying, 'We need to get a move on.'

'Where are we going?'

'It's a surprise.'

Gracie loved surprises. She didn't get many of them, but since Lucas had come into her life, every day was a surprise, from the way her tummy turned over when she saw him unexpectedly, to the little gifts he gave her, and to the way her desire for him threatened to overwhelm her. On more than one occasion she'd tried to drag him into her bed, only for him to hang back. She wondered what he was waiting for. As far as she was concerned the time was more than right, and she worried that he didn't want to take this final step and make love to her because he was leaving.

She didn't care; she wanted all of him. She'd deal with her broken heart when the time came. They hadn't said they loved each other and she didn't think they would, but deep down she knew how she felt about him, and she was fairly certain he felt the same way about her. Once those three little words were spoken though, there would be no going back.

But today was her birthday and Lucas was taking her out. She didn't want to think sad thoughts; she wanted to enjoy her day and fill it with wonderful memories, so she could relive them once Lucas had gone.

'It's quite a journey,' he warned, as she buckled up her seat belt.

'I wondered why you wanted to pick me up at seven o'clock in the morning,' Gracie said.

'Don't worry, we'll stop off en route for coffee and breakfast. You'll need to keep your strength up for the day ahead.'

Intrigued Gracie wondered where they were going as they drove across country, passing through towns such as Newtown and Shrewsbury. By the time they'd driven through Telford, she guessed they were on their way to Birmingham.

In some respects, she was disappointed, because she didn't particularly like large cities, and she certainly didn't want to do any shopping, which was the only reason she could think off for going to one. She was sure she'd enjoy herself regardless, but she really would have preferred a nice long walk by a river, followed by a pub lunch, or even a day at the beach. Shopping wasn't really her thing.

However, she rapidly changed her mind when she spotted a sign that said *Vintage Clothes and Textile Fair*, and she turned to Lucas, her eyes wide as he drove into a parking space and cut the engine. He was grinning from ear to ear.

'Is that where we're going?' she asked.

'Yep.'

'Is this for work, for UnderCover?'

'Nope.'

'For *me*?'

'Who else would it be for? It's certainly not for me, although I don't care where I am, as long as I'm with you. This is your birthday, and I wanted you to do something you'd enjoy. You can blame Catrin; she put the idea in my head.'

'I could kiss her,' Gracie said, clapping her hands together.

'I'd prefer it if you kissed me,' Lucas said, so she did precisely that, until the gear stick became so uncomfortable as it poked her in the side that she had no option but to let him go. Besides, she was desperate to get into the fair and have a good look around.

It was absolutely huge. There was stall after stall as far as the eye could see, and she didn't know where to start. She dashed from one to another, like a puppy off its leash, before she settled and began to methodically go up and down the aisles. She had no intention of buying anything, even though so many things caught her eye, but just the fact that she was here amongst all those lovely coats, dresses, skirts, shoes, and bags was exhilarating. She jumped up and down on the spot and clapped her hands again.

'I can't believe you brought me here! This is wonderful. Thank you so much. You don't know how much this means to me.'

Lucas put his arm around her and hugged her close, whispering into her hair, 'I think I do.'

She looked up at him, and the love in his eyes stole her breath and stabbed her in the chest. Oh my God, how was she going to let him go when the time came? She didn't think her heart could bear it.

Slightly more subdued, Gracie continued with her exploration of the fair, and although she wanted to lose herself in all the wonderful textiles for sale, half of her attention was on the man at her side, who followed her from stall to stall with uncomplaining patience.

Finally, it was inevitable that she would run out of steam, and they headed for one of the many food stands for a drink and a welcome snack.

'Have you seen anything you fancy?' Lucas asked her.

Apart from you, you mean, she nearly said. 'Loads of things.'

'Anything in particular?'

'Too many to list.' Although she was thoroughly enjoying looking, she had no intention of buying anything, even though some of the fabrics were to die for. She did however manage to take away quite a few ideas, and she couldn't wait to get started on them – it would be something to keep her occupied in the long weeks and months ahead without Lucas in her life.

Tired after a full day and feeling overwhelmed, Gracie was happy to get back in the car, but her birthday wasn't over yet and Lucas had another card up his sleeve.

It was only when she realised they were taking a different route back and she questioned him about it, that Lucas told her he'd booked dinner in Ludlow.

'I've done something else,' he admitted, looking incredibly sheepish, and Gracie shot him a concerned glance.

'What have you done?'

'I've booked us a room.'

Gracie was taken aback. She certainly hadn't expected that. She was also rather put out, as she hadn't brought anything with her: no toothbrush, no change of underwear. Not only that, she would have appreciated being asked first.

Although she desperately wanted to share his bed, this seemed a little clinical. She knew it was supposed to be a nice surprise, but he'd taken the 'nice' out of it and she was just left with 'surprise'.

'Actually, I've booked two rooms,' he said, 'And I've also packed an overnight bag for you. To be honest, it wasn't me who packed it, it was Catrin.'

'Catrin? When did she do that?' Gracie was beginning to mellow a little at the news that Lucas wasn't assuming she was going to spend the night with him, and she wondered what Catrin had packed for her.

'When you were at work yesterday. She did say you wouldn't mind.' Lucas looked worried, as well he might. 'She told me she thought it was a wonderful idea and that you'd love it. You don't, do you?'

'Let's see, shall we? I do like surprises but perhaps this one is a surprise too far.'

Lucas manoeuvred the car through the narrow streets of Ludlow, turned left under an archway and drove into a court-yard car park. The building the courtyard was attached to was extremely old, with black Tudor beams and white wattling. It looked absolutely gorgeous.

Inside the hotel, Gracie gazed around in awe. The reception area had wood panelling and old slate flag stones. The reception desk itself was huge and dark, and was a very impressive piece of furniture. A plaque on the wall told her that the building originally dated from 1348.

They were taken up a very rickety staircase which creaked and groaned underneath their feet, and led along a short corridor, where the receptionist stopped and indicated two doors next to each other.

'They're both exactly the same, both en suite, so it's up to you which one you'd like to take.' The man smiled at Gracie, and she smiled hesitantly back. He handed her a key after opening the door, and said in a professional voice, 'I hope you enjoy your stay. Breakfast is served from seven a.m. onwards in the dining room.'

She thanked him, pushed the door open wide and stuck her head inside. 'Oh my God,' she breathed, her eyes nearly popping out of her head. 'It's got a four-poster bed!' She pointed vigorously into the room, unable to believe her eyes.

'I know, I booked it, remember?' Lucas was smiling at her, still a little warily.

'Have you got a four-poster in yours?'

'I hope so, because that's what it was described as, and that guy just said the rooms were identical. Do you want to come and have a look?'

She nodded, and was as impressed with his room as she was with her own. Leaving him to freshen up, Gracie hastened back into her room to have a look at what Catrin had packed for her, praying that it wasn't too outlandish or too inappropriate.

To her delight, she discovered a little bag of toiletries, all of them brand new, including a toothbrush and toothpaste, her best set of underwear (how Catrin knew it was her best set Gracie had no idea) plus a gorgeous floor-length silk nightie, which definitely did not belong to Gracie. She ran her fingers across the fabric, feeling its delectable smoothness. Catrin had also packed a pair of pumps, a pair of skinny jeans, a pretty top and a cardigan, which Gracie assumed she was to wear tomorrow for the journey home.

She'd also packed the most wonderful dress Gracie had ever seen. It was a deep emerald green with a boat neckline, very fitted at the waist and with a flowing skirt. It wasn't too dressy, so she wouldn't feel ridiculous wearing it in a restaurant, but on the other hand it wasn't the sort of thing she'd wear to pop to the supermarket for a loaf of bread. Catrin had teamed it with a pair of low-heeled tan court shoes.

A tentative knock on the door made her jump, and she carefully draped the dress on the bed before she went to answer it.

'I've booked a table in the restaurant for eight o'clock,' Lucas said. 'If that suits you?'

'That's fine,' Gracie said. It was only six thirty, which would give her enough time to have a bath, which was simply enormous and had some complimentary smellies on a little shelf just above the taps, wrestle her hair into submission, and reapply a slick of mascara to her eyelashes.

It was only after she'd soaked in the bath, emerging with slightly crinkly fingertips and glowing from the heat, that she noticed Catrin had popped a little note inside the toiletry bag.

Gracie smiled when she read it. It said *Go for it* with a large *x*. There was something else inside too: a tiny bottle of perfume, a bronze eye shadow, and a lipstick.

Gracie eyed the latter two items with distrust. She hadn't worn eye shadow for a very long time and lipstick usually ended up smeared all over her teeth, and that was before a drink had even passed her lips. Then there was the meal, and maybe some more delectable kisses. The lipstick didn't stand a hope in hell in staying on, so she might as well not bother. She'd have a go with the eye shadow though, with the proviso that she could always rub it off if she looked like a clown.

She had just finished raking her fingers through her hair and teasing her curls into submission, when there was another knock at the door.

'Come in,' she called, and Lucas stuck his head round the door. His mouth opened when he saw her, and he let out a low whistle.

'You look good enough to eat,' he said.

Feeling emboldened by the dress, the eye shadow and the mascara, Gracie said 'If you're lucky, you can have me for dessert.' Then she did her usual blushing trick.

His voice was low when he said, 'I might take you up on that.'

Croakily Gracie replied, 'I wish you would.'

In three strides he was standing in front of her, and a second later she was in his arms, melting into his embrace. His lips found hers and teased her gently, his tongue seeking hers. She deliberately stepped back, falling onto the bed, taking Lucas with her, and the weight of him as he lay on top of her send deep bolts of desire coursing through her, and she let out a little whimper.

Immediately Lucas raised himself up taking his weight off her. 'Are you OK? Did I hurt you?'

'No, get back down here: I haven't finished with you yet.'

His eyes were dark pits of hunger, and she shivered – he really did intend to eat her all up, and she couldn't wait. With a low groan his lips found hers again and his hands roved over her curves, and Gracie wanted nothing more than to feel him naked against her.

Dinner would have to wait.

Chapter 33

Lucas

'Thank you for the best birthday present ever,' Gracie said over breakfast the following morning.

Lucas was absolutely ravenous. Not only had they totally missed dinner last night, but he'd expended far more energy than he normally would have in bed, several times. And again, this morning. He couldn't get enough of her, and it had been a wrench having to shower and get dressed for breakfast. But his stomach was being particularly demanding, and coffee, bacon and eggs were not to be denied.

'It was nothing,' Lucas said, with a lascivious smirk and a waggle of his eyebrows.

'I was talking about the visit to the vintage fair,' she retorted, then burst out laughing at his crestfallen expression.

'For a second there I thought I had lost my touch.'

'Oh no, your touch is perfectly fine, thank you very much,' Gracie said, and Lucas felt a surge of pure lust shoot through him.

Good God, this woman was so incredibly sexy. She was also utterly, utterly gorgeous and he couldn't stop looking at her and smiling. To an outsider they must look like a couple in love.

For his part, it was true. His feelings for her had been growing ever since they'd met, and after last night he knew he was in love.

He thought about telling her of his intention to remain in Applewell, but he wasn't sure how she'd react. He knew she really liked him, but did she like him *enough*? Despite what Catrin had said about Gracie not wanting to give herself to him because he wasn't going to be around, he wasn't entirely sure he believed it. She had given herself to him last night, all right, and it had been wonderful, but had she done so in the belief that in two weeks he'd be gone? Would she have made love with him if she'd known he was going to be a permanent feature in the village?

There would be time enough to tell her in the next week or so, after he'd handed his notice in and started looking for another job. At the moment his focus was on sorting out the designer sales website for UnderCover and doing the massive amount of organisation which went on behind the scenes to ensure that any item of significant value was sent to a central location, where it could be assessed and prepared for sale. It was a mammoth undertaking; not so much because of the volume of items, but because of the number of shops and their scattered locations, and also because of the number of existing shop staff who would need to receive additional training. This was his legacy to Jonas and to UnderCover, and he wanted to break the back of the project before he left.

At the moment he could do a great deal of this work from home (his mother's home, not his flat in London) and he'd already managed several meetings remotely, rather than having to travel to the city for them. But at some point in the not-too-distant future, everything would be up and running and he'd be expected to return to his original post. Which was why he needed to sort out another job ASAP.

'I've been thinking about Nora's wedding,' Lucas said, dipping a piece of toast into golden runny yolk. 'Will you come with me as my plus one?'

'Will Nora mind?'

'I shouldn't think so.'

'Don't you think you'd better check with her first?' Gracie asked.

'I suppose I should. But assuming she's happy with that, will you come with me?'

'Of course I will. But I've got to warn you, I'm not too keen on big public events. I probably won't be very good company.'

'You're always good company,' he countered. 'And I don't care if you don't say a word to anyone, as long as you're by my side.'

He knew he was being soppy, but he didn't care. He meant every word of it. And he wished he had time to show her just how much he meant it, but it was already seven forty-five and he knew Gracie was anxious to get back to open the shop. They probably wouldn't arrive in Applewell for at least an hour and a half, if not two, but Monday mornings were usually quiet, so he hoped she wasn't going to miss much trade.

He didn't envy her, thinking how tired she might be because of their lack of sleep, but when he thought of the reason for it, he sniggered. When she asked him what he was laughing about and he told her, she threw a crust of toast at him and stuck her nose in the air.

He was more than happy to see her nod off during the car journey home, and it was only when they were about fifteen minutes away from Applewell that he gently woke her up.

'I want to spend the rest of the day with you, but before you say anything, I know you can't, so I'll see you later if that's OK?'

She yawned and clambered out of the car. 'Come round to mine. Bring food.'

'I'll go one better than that,' he said. 'I'll cook for you. I'm assuming you do have pots and pans and things?'

'Don't be silly,' she said, leaning back into the car to kiss him soundly on the lips. 'Thank you so much for yesterday,' she added. 'I had the most amazing time.'

'So did I,' he said, and he absolutely meant it.

—

Thankfully his mother was at work when he arrived home. He'd told her that he was going away for the night for Gracie's birthday, and he'd also told her that he'd booked separate rooms, just to prevent the knowing looks, but he was glad to have the house to himself for once and not to have to answer her questions.

He was too tired and too full of Gracie to think straight, but nevertheless he plugged his laptop in and began to work. Or rather he tried to, but he found himself on Rightmove checking out properties for sale and to rent. To his disappointment there wasn't a great deal, but he supposed he could always live with his mum for the time being. After his trawl through the property pages, he ended up on various job sites, scrolling endlessly and feeling rather dispirited.

He broke up the day by popping into the village for some supplies for this evening. He planned on cooking teriyaki salmon, and debated whether to pick up a bottle of wine to go with it but decided he wouldn't and grabbed some sparkling water instead.

Back home, he finally got his work head on and had been hard at it for a couple of hours when his mother came in. She looked absolutely shattered, so he made her a cup of tea and began preparing supper for her.

'What are we having?' she asked, wandering into the kitchen and leaning against the door jamb.

'You're having one of your favourites – sausage, mash and onion gravy – but I'm going to Gracie's house and cooking her a meal there,' he said.

His mother gave him a knowing smile. 'You're getting on very well with Gracie,' she pointed out.

Lucas made a noncommittal sound.

'Did you have a nice time yesterday?'

'Yes, thank you, it was lovely. Gracie really enjoyed her visit to the fair.'

'What about last night? How was dinner?' Lucas couldn't meet his mother's eye, and she sighed. 'I hope you know what you're doing,' she said. 'I'd hate to see Gracie get hurt.'

'What about me? I can get hurt, too.'

His mother tilted her head to the side. 'Is that what's going to happen when you go back to London?'

Should he tell her his plans now?

He supposed he had to, because what if he handed his notice in, then told his mother he was staying in Applewell and she wasn't happy about him living in her house? Despite her insistence that this would always be his home, it might be a very different prospect living with him for the foreseeable future.

'Mum, I've got something to tell—'

The front door slammed open, making both of them jump and Vivien clapped a hand to her mouth and let out a small cry.

'Goodness, whatever is the matter?' she demanded as Nora flew into the kitchen, pulling a crying Ruby along behind her. 'What's happened?'

'Castle Hotel have just phoned: there's a problem with the room. We can't have the ceremony and the reception there, so they've moved us somewhere else. They want me to go and check it out.' She wrung her hands. 'What am I going to do? The wedding is two weeks away. *Two* weeks! I ask you! How could they do this to me!'

Lucas was so startled at her outburst that he didn't know what to say. Fortunately, their mother had more of a grasp on the situation.

'I don't think they're actually doing it to *you*, as such,' Vivian pointed out. 'I doubt if they want to change things unless they absolutely have to. Why don't you go and have a chat with them and see what's what?'

'Ianto is at work!'

'You can go without him, can't you?' their mother asked.

'But I want him to see it,' Nora wailed.

'Do you think he'd be that bothered?' Vivian asked wryly.

'No, but that's not the point. What am I going to do? I had the room planned out and everything.'

'How about if I come with you?' His mother sent Lucas an apologetic look. 'I can eat when I get home,' she said.

'What about Ruby? I don't want to take her with me; she's done nothing but grizzle all afternoon.'

'You can leave her with me,' Lucas said. He knelt until he was at eye level with his niece, who had stopped crying but was still unhappy. 'We'll have a great time, won't we?'

Ruby nodded a little uncertainly.

'You won't grizzle for your uncle Lucas, will you?'

Ruby nodded, this time with more conviction.

'You *will*? If you do, you'll make *me* cry,' Lucas threatened. Ruby giggled. 'I tell you what,' he said, thinking that, depending on how long it took Nora and his mother to drive to the Castle Hotel, sort out the issue and come back again, he might have to amend his plans to go to Gracie's house this evening. 'Why don't we ask Gracie if she'd like to come over, and she can help keep you company while I cook us some dinner? Would you like that?'

Ruby nodded once more.

Nora sent him a grateful look. 'Thank you,' she said. 'But please don't feed her too many sweets.' She turned to her mother. 'I know you've got a cupboard full, but I'll never get her to bed if she's had too many E numbers.'

Gracie, to his immense relief, was more than happy to come round to his mum's house. She even brought some scraps of material and glue, having popped into the newsagents on the way to buy some big sheets of paper.

'I thought we could make some fabric pictures,' Gracie told Ruby, who was rifling through the multicoloured pieces of material, sequins and buttons in a very determined way.

'I like these colours,' Ruby said, holding up a bright pink and a neon blue square of material. 'I want to make a mermaid picture.'

'You can make whatever picture you like,' Gracie told her. 'And I'll help you. How does that sound? That'll leave Uncle Lucas free to make us some food.'

Lucas had hastily reassessed the dinner situation, coming to the conclusion that pizza was probably a better bet for a small child, because otherwise he had no idea what she would or wouldn't eat.

'How about pizza?' he asked.

'Yay!' Ruby clapped her hands together.

He'd found a Margherita pizza in the freezer, and his mother had a well-stocked cupboard so he was sure he could wrestle together a relatively healthy meal with the addition of some fresh toppings. He heard from Jonas that it was a nightmare to get kids to eat vegetables, so he'd chop up some peppers very finely and sprinkle them across the top, and after that she could choose what she wanted on her own pizza, within reason. And of course, Gracie would help too, he hoped.

With Gracie entertaining Ruby and Lucas busying himself with dinner, he had a sudden flash of how this picture could look several years down the line: Gracie wouldn't be sitting with his niece but with their own child, and his heart constricted. It was an image he would very much like to see come true.

Determined to make sure it would, Lucas could clearly see his future in Applewell, with Gracie firmly in it.

Chapter 34

Gracie

'What on earth is the matter with you?' Catrin asked, as Gracie lurched through the door of UnderCover with a large bag in her hands. Gracie knew she had a face like thunder, but she couldn't help it. The last few weeks had been absolutely perfect. Which made facing a future without Lucas in it, sheer hell.

'Is Lucas here?' she asked.

'No, he isn't. He's working from his mum's house. Something to do with setting up an online shop for the more expensive items. But you know all about that, considering you were the brains behind it.' Catrin smiled gently at her.

'Don't talk to me about brains,' Gracie said. It was Lucas picking her brains that had started all this. She knew she was being grumpy, but the knowledge that he would only be an Applewell for another ten days or so was weighing heavily on her.

'I brought you these,' she said, handing Catrin the bag. It was full of her scrappy fabric dolls for UnderCover to sell.

'That's brilliant, thank you,' Catrin said. 'We're down to the last two. You wouldn't believe how popular they are.'

Gracie would. Even if she did say so herself, they were lovely little things. Any little girl would be happy to have one. She thought of the doll she'd made especially for Ruby. She'd dressed it as a fairy princess, and she'd tell Ruby that was how the world saw her when she gave it to her on Nora's wedding day.

'It's Lucas, isn't it?' Catrin asked. 'What's he done? I thought you two were getting on like a house on fire.'

'We are, that's the problem.' She burst into tears.

Catrin dropped the bag and hurried over to her, flinging her arms around her and dragging her close for a comforting cuddle. 'Aw, sweetie, I wish I could do something to help.'

'No one can do anything,' Gracie said through her sniffles. 'I just didn't think it would hurt this much, and he hasn't even gone yet. How am I going to live without him?'

'You will, the pain will go.'

'When?'

'I can't answer that. But it will ease; it always does.'

'I don't want it to.'

Catrin patted her on the back and murmured inconsequential words in her ear as Gracie sobbed. 'It'll be all right,' she murmured, over and over.

But Gracie knew it was never going to be all right again. She would always carry the pain of loving Lucas in her heart. It might ease, but she knew without a doubt that it would always be there.

She should have listened to her head when it told her that there would be nothing but heartache if she fell in love with Lucas, but she hadn't. Instead, she'd thought of how fragile life was, and how she didn't want to get to the end of hers and think *what if*? She had been so determined to experience love for herself, that she hadn't seriously considered the consequences.

That was because she'd never had a broken heart, and she hadn't been aware of how much it would hurt. Hers was breaking piece by little piece, and she'd never felt pain like it before. She wished she could say she'd never feel pain like it again, but she had a feeling this would be an ongoing situation and one which she'd never truly recover from.

After going through several tissues and drinking a restorative cup of tea, Gracie felt ready to face the world again, and she announced that she had to get back as she'd only intended to be out of the shop for five minutes, but over half an hour had already gone by.

Catrin gave her another hug, but just as Gracie was about to leave, she clapped her hand to her mouth.

'Hang on a second, I've got something for you,' she said, and scuttled out the back, returning with a very large bag stuffed full of all kinds of interesting things.

When Gracie felt the weight of it, she immediately told Catrin off. 'You shouldn't be lifting this,' she said. 'Not in your condition. I hope you haven't been overdoing it.'

'I'm pregnant, not ill,' Catrin said, looking hastily around in case someone had come in and overheard her.

'I don't care,' Gracie said. 'You still shouldn't be lifting anything heavy, doing anything strenuous, or overdoing things at all. Anyway, how are you?' she asked guiltily. 'I'm sorry, it's been all me, me, me.'

'OK, I suppose. I'm definitely not blooming yet. Still feeling sick and incredibly tired all the time.'

'I'm not surprised. You're growing a whole new human in there.' Gracie patted Catrin's stomach affectionately.

'I am, aren't I?' Catrin's smile was radiant.

Gracie held onto her own smile until she was outside, then despondency draped over her again like a big black cloak, and she vowed she would try and lighten up before she saw Lucas this evening. The last thing he needed was to remember her with a sour look on her face.

Crikey, this bag was heavy Gracie said to herself, as she walked back to A Stitch in Time. It was almost dragging her arm out of its socket and she shifted it to the other hand, the plastic biting into her fingers. Abruptly she was yanked backwards, and she cursed when she saw the reason for it. The bag had snagged on the wheel of someone's shopping trolley and had torn, and clothes were now spilling out all over the pavement.

'Damn and blast!' she muttered, bending over to pick them up and stuffing them back in the tattered bag.

'Let me help,' Lucas said, appearing at her side, and she shot him a grateful smile. 'Here, hold these, I thought we could have a cup of tea and some shortbread biscuits, so I popped into the bakery for some.'

He shoved a paper bag at her and she slipped it into her pocket, hoping the biscuits would still be intact when she pulled them back out again.

'Isn't this from UnderCover?' Lucas asked as he tried to stuff a curtain back into the bag and failing miserably.

'Yes, it's all from UnderCover,' Gracie said. 'Wait there, I've got some black plastic bags in the shop; I'll go and get them.'

'Hang on...' Lucas was frowning, and Gracie halted. 'I thought I'd put this in the textile bin – the one for the recycling company. This, too...' He held up a pair of dungarees with so many paint splashes on them, there was barely an inch of faded blue denim to be seen. 'Where are you taking them?' he asked. The frown was still there.

'To A Stitch in Time, of course.'

'There's no "of course" about it. How much did Catrin charge you for this little lot?'

Gracie blinked. 'Nothing. She gives me anything that's going to be thrown out and I—'

'*She doesn't charge you for them?*' He sounded incredulous.

'No, as I was saying—'

'I don't believe it. This should not be happening. I know UnderCover doesn't receive much for the unsellable items, but not much is better than nothing at all. You know how strongly I feel about the charity and how hard I work to raise funds for it. Why would you do something like this?'

Gracie was confused. Surely these things were going to be thrown away? She thought she'd been doing the right thing by salvaging what she could, but clearly not. Did Catrin know that she shouldn't have been giving Gracie this stuff for nothing? What was it worth, anyway? Surely not much?

'I'll fetch a bag,' she said stiffly.

'Don't bother, I can manage.' Lucas scooped everything up, sleeves and trouser legs dangling.

They stared at each other for a second, Gracie wondering what on earth was going on. Already feeling fragile, she thought she might burst into tears. Then he walked away.

No 'see you later', no 'I'll call you'. Nothing.

Her eyes stinging, Gracie trudged back to A Stitch in Time, her throat constricting as she tried not to cry. She felt weak and unsteady, as though she'd been steamrollered.

OK, so maybe she should have paid for the stuff Catrin had given her, but he needn't have been so mean about it. She wasn't to know. Besides which, he'd not given her a chance to explain.

By the time she burst through the shop's door and locked it behind her, anger was superseding tears. How dare he! It wasn't as though she didn't support UnderCover. In fact, the dolls and other repairs more than compensated for the measly amount that would be got from the textile recyclers, and surely repairing and mending was better than using more resources? He'd acted as though she was stealing from the homeless.

If that was how he thought of her, she'd seriously misjudged him. All it had taken was a simple misunderstanding for him to show how little regard he had for her. Now that he'd taken her to bed and had his wicked way with her, it was easy for him to discard her. Had he, in fact, been waiting for an opportunity like this to end it? It would save him the bother of an emotional farewell, and he might even be fearful that she'd be all clingy and desperate.

Her heart might be breaking, but she told herself she was glad he was buggering off in ten days, because she never wanted to see him again.

Chapter 35

Lucas

Lucas couldn't believe what he'd just seen. It was blatant. Gracie had even admitted that she'd been given those items for nothing. He really wasn't sure how to feel about that. Perhaps his reaction was over the top, but he was so shocked at her deceit: one minute she was praising him for his passion for UnderCover, then behind his back she was taking money out of the till. That might be a bit of an exaggeration, but technically it was true.

Bartering was all well and good, as was helping a friend out, but Gracie should have been paying for these things, and Catrin should know better than to just give them away.

Maybe if he hadn't seen the red coat draped over a tailor's dummy in Gracie's workroom, he might not have been quite so annoyed. But it was clear that she had taken the coat, repaired it, and had made a profit from it. Despite her protestations, she probably *had* sold it on eBay. No wonder she knew all about selling clothes on the site – it looked like she had been doing it to supplement her income. And he still harboured the suspicion that she might be sharing the profits with Catrin.

Just wait until he got his hands on the shop's manager. He'd certainly give her a piece of his mind. He was angrier at Catrin than he was with Gracie, because Catrin should know better.

He honestly couldn't believe it. After everything he'd shared with Gracie, she had done this to him. There was no point in telling himself not to take it personally: how else was he meant to take it? The woman he loved had been taking money out of the charity he had put his heart and soul into for over a decade, the same charity he had to thank for giving him a chance when he was living rough on the streets, cold, starving and friendless apart from Effron.

Feeling more betrayed and sad rather than angry, which had been his initial reaction, he hurried back to UnderCover; he and Catrin needed to have a serious talk.

Catrin was hunched over the counter with its glass top, arranging the bits of jewellery in it. She looked up when she saw him and smiled.

He glared at her, and her smile faded.

'What's wrong?' she asked.

Lucas marched up to the counter and deposited his armful of clothes onto it. Catrin flinched. 'This! *This* is what's wrong. Care to explain?'

'I…' Her colour was up, and she looked worried.

Ignoring her stuttering, Lucas dived in. 'This has got to stop. You might think it's OK to give this stuff away, but actually it's theft. It's no different from taking a pair of trousers off the rack, and just handing them to somebody. As soon as we are given a donation, the item becomes the property of UnderCover. You're paid to run the shop, to make a profit for UnderCover, not to give stuff away to your friends whenever you feel like it.'

Catrin's hand was on her chest, and her mouth opened and closed, but no sound came out.

Lucas ploughed on. 'It's people like you and Gracie who are part of the problem. The charity needs every penny it can get. Yet here you are, giving away some of the proceeds. I know we don't get much for each item, not even for a whole tonne of unusable textiles, but we do get *something*, and that something might very well be enough for a meal for a homeless person. You're lucky I don't take this to head office. And don't tell me this is the first time it's happened, because I know it isn't. The very first day I was here, there was a bin full of stuff, and I distinctly remember a red coat with a torn sleeve.' He shook his head, disappointment riding him hard. 'Do you know where I discovered it next?' He didn't give Catrin a chance to answer. 'I saw it in Gracie's house. She had clearly repaired it. How much did she get for it? Did she share some of that with you? Or were you being altruistic in helping out a friend?'

He stopped, having run out of steam. He hadn't felt quite so disgusted in a very long time. No doubt when he had time to think calmly and rationally about this, he'd feel differently, and he'd probably have to apologise.

His reaction was rather over the top, he was forced to admit, but neither Gracie nor Catrin had seen what he had seen, or had experienced what he had experienced. Being scared, frozen, sleeping on nothing but a sheet of cardboard between you and the cold ground, unable to remember the last time you ate… it was no joke.

Catrin, her eyes filled with tears, emerged from behind the counter and sidled around him. He wondered if she was just going to walk out, and he was about to ask her not to when she halted by a newly replenished shelf of rag dolls. He only had time to wonder who had brought them in, when Catrin picked up the nearest one and hurled it at him.

'Do you know what this is?' she demanded, her tears flowing freely. 'This is a ragdoll made out of scraps of material. Who do you know who recycles scraps of material? *Hmm?*' She put her hands on her hips and glared at him. 'Gracie, that's who, and UnderCover doesn't give her a penny for them. She makes them in exchange for me giving her all those textiles you're so precious about. And I can tell you something else – the shop makes far more of a profit from these dolls than we ever would from dirty babygros, or odd socks. And there's something else.' She stamped past him and went out into the backroom, a furious expression on her face, and he couldn't decide whether she was crying because she was upset or because she was angry.

Lucas's mouth was open, his mind whirling furiously.

He should have known. He should have guessed. The dolls had Gracie's signature all over them. They were exactly the kind of things she made. Why hadn't he seen it? How had he got it so wrong?

He waited anxiously for Catrin to come back. He'd apologise to her, then he'd apologise to Gracie. He just hoped both of them would forgive him. He shouldn't have jumped to conclusions.

Where was she? What was Catrin doing out there?

He waited for another few minutes, but there was no sign of her.

So he went to the back room to look for her. His heart was in his boots, as he thought of what an idiot he'd been. He'd jumped in to accuse and condemn without knowing the full story. He should have just asked.

Ready to give her a grovelling apology, he stuck his head round the door.

Catrin was sitting on a chair with the red coat in her lap, the same one he'd seen in Gracie's house, and he felt even more of a fool.

Then he glanced up at her face, an abject apology on his tongue, but what he saw when he looked at her shocked him beyond measure.

Her eyes were brimming with tears, her face shockingly pale. She wore such an expression of fear, that he curled his hands into fists at his own stupidity. My God, what had he done?

Her mouth was working, but no words came out.

'Catrin, I am so, so sorry. What the hell must you think of me? I should have just asked, instead of jumping to conclusions. It was inexcusable and unforgivable.'

She didn't look at him, she just sat there with the coat in her lap, tears dripping down her face and onto the fabric.

'Catrin? Catrin! Look, I'm sorry, I honestly didn't mean to upset you. Please don't cry. Please.'

Finally, he seemed to get through to her, and she turned haunted eyes to his. 'I'm bleeding,' she said.

266

'What?' It took him a moment for her words to sink in, and when they did he scanned her swiftly, not seeing any obvious injury. 'Have you hurt yourself? I can't see any blood.'

She hitched in a sobbing breath. 'I'm pregnant.'

Oh, shit. 'What should I do?' He had absolutely zero experience of pregnant women. Should he call an ambulance? Should he take her straight to the hospital himself?

'Phone Gracie,' she wailed. 'And Gareth.'

'OK, I can do that, then what?'

Catrin shook her head. 'Just phone them.' Her fingers twisted together, the motion relentless.

Lucas took out his phone and dialled Gracie's number. It rang a couple of times, then she dropped the call. 'Damn and blast,' he growled. He'd have to go round there, but he didn't want to leave Catrin on her own.

Next, he tried Gareth, who thankfully answered after a couple of rings.

'I can't talk now, Lucas,' he said. 'I'm in the middle of something.'

'You're going to have to talk. In fact, you're going to have to come to UnderCover. It's Catrin – she says she's pregnant and she's bleeding.'

There was a second of silence, then Gareth said abruptly, 'On my way.' The call ended.

'Gareth is on his way, but Gracie isn't picking up her phone,' he told Catrin, even though she'd been sitting right there and had heard every word.

'Go and fetch her.'

'I can't leave you on your own.'

'It doesn't matter whether I'm on my own or not, I'm still bleeding. You can't do anything useful; the only thing you can do is to fetch Gracie.'

Having no choice, Lucas dashed to the door, fumbling at the 'Closed' sign as he shot through it and ran down the pavement, thanking God that A Stitch in Time was only a couple of shops away, so he didn't have far to go.

It too had a 'Closed' sign on the door, and when he tried to push it open he discovered it was firmly locked. Lucas, adrenalin making his hands shake, hammered on the glass so hard he thought it might shatter.

Gracie immediately darted onto the shop floor, her face a mask of fury, her hair in wild corkscrews around her head, her eyes flashing sparks. 'Get lost!' she yelled at him.

He shook his head and rattled the door handle. 'Open up,' he cried. 'I need to speak to you.'

'I think you've said everything I want to hear,' she shouted back, giving him a cold stare.

Lucas banged on the door again. 'It's Catrin. She's bleeding,' he yelled, not caring who heard. All he wanted to do was to persuade Gracie to go to her friend.

Gracie's mouth dropped open and she shook her head. 'Catrin?'

'Yes, Catrin. She needs you *now*.'

Gracie dashed back into the stockroom, emerging a second later with her bag and the shop keys. She flew to the door, opened it and pushed him out of the way, then ran up the pavement, with Lucas hot on her heels.

Please, let her be OK, he prayed silently, *please, let the baby be OK*. This was all his fault; he'd yelled at her without knowing the full facts, but now Catrin might lose her baby and if she did, he'd be to blame.

If anything happened to her or her baby, Lucas didn't know how he'd ever forgive himself.

Chapter 36

Gracie

Gracie kept her worry in check, not wanting Catrin to see. She had taken one look at her friend's devastated face and said everything she could think of to reassure her; however, not knowing a great deal about pregnancy, she wasn't sure whether she was saying the right thing or even making any kind of sense.

Her relief when Gareth barrelled through the door and took over was immense. She helped the almost hysterical Catrin into the car, then stood forlornly on the pavement watching Gareth drive off far too fast, and prayed that everything would be OK. She remained there for a moment chewing her lip, waiting for her pulse to return to normal. What a terrible thing to happen.

Suddenly remembering, she rounded on Lucas who was hovering behind her.

'It's your fault,' she said. 'All your fault. I know what you did. You came back here and accused her of... I don't know *what* you accused her of... but you accused her of *something*. She was sitting there with that red coat in her lap, so don't tell me you didn't have a go at her. And now you might have made her lose the baby.'

'I know.' Lucas's voice was small, and she could barely hear him.

'Is that all you've got to say for yourself?' she demanded.

'I'm sorry, so desperately sorry,' he said.

'That's not going to help matters if she loses that baby, is it?' Gracie's heart was thumping madly, and her breathing was coming in short jerky gasps. 'Get out of my sight, just get out of my sight. Leave me alone. I never want to see you again!'

It was Gracie's turn to cry in great big sobs as she stormed off back to A Stitch in Time, leaving him standing there. Perhaps he'd bugger off back to London now and save her the heartache of bumping into him again. She was damn sure that Catrin wouldn't want to set eyes on him again, and once Gareth found out what had happened he'd probably knock Lucas's block off. It would serve him right.

It was time to face facts — Lucas Granger was not the man she'd thought he was.

—

'Are you sure the baby is OK?' Gracie demanded. Catrin had told her at least three times, but Gracie wanted to hear her say it again. Phone lines could be dodgy and she might have misheard.

'The baby is fine. He's got a strong heartbeat, and I saw him moving.'

'You're having a *boy*?'

'I don't know, I'm just saying "he" for the sake of calling the baby something.' Catrin sounded giddy with relief, and Gracie was feeling a little giddy herself.

'Are they keeping you in?' she asked.

'No, I'm free to go home. I'm just waiting for some more folic acid tablets, and then I can leave.'

'How are you feeling?'

'Relieved, scared, excited, absolutely knackered.'

'I'm so sorry, Catrin. This is all my fault. You nearly lost your baby because of me.'

'Don't be ridiculous. Apparently, it's extremely common. That's why it's advisable not to say anything until about the twelve-week mark. Mother Nature has decided by then whether the foetus is viable or not. The doctor said there is often bleeding at around this time. In fact, you can be spotting right up until you give birth. It doesn't stop me worrying though. I've never been so scared in all my life. I felt sure I was going to lose him.'

'I still feel responsible,' Gracie insisted. 'If I hadn't taken the waste fabric off you, you never would have lifted that bag, and Lucas would never have seen it and had a go at you.'

'It wasn't his fault either, Gracie.'

'You might be able to forgive him, but I can't.'

'The way he spoke to me was unforgivable, and he didn't give me a chance to explain before he launched into his tirade, but you can't blame him for me bleeding. As I said, it's rather common. It would have happened regardless and I wasn't feeling all that wonderful this morning, anyway. So that was probably the lead up to it. If you're intent on not forgiving him, that's up to you, but don't make it about me nearly losing the baby, because it wasn't his fault. I didn't lose it. I'm fine; the baby is fine.'

'He wasn't very nice to me, either. But it was inexcusable the way he spoke to you, a pregnant woman.'

'To be fair to him, he didn't know I was pregnant. I agree he should have given me a chance to explain, but look at it from his point of view. In a way, he's right: it *is* theft.'

'But if he hadn't been so shouty, you would have been able to tell him about the scrappy dolls and the repairs,' Gracie pointed out. 'Sorry... I get so angry just thinking about it.'

Gracie could tell that Catrin was smiling when she said, 'So I gather. Anyway, just to let you know, I won't be in work for the next few days. I've already arranged with Lucas that he's to run the shop until I'm back on my feet.'

'You've *spoken* to him?'

'Yes, he phoned Gareth and told him exactly what had happened. He blames himself, you know.'

'So he should,' Gracie retorted.

'He told Gareth he's going to apologise to you, too,' Catrin said.

'He needn't bother. I don't want to hear anything he has to say.'

'That's as may be and I can understand you're hurt, but at least let him apologise. He knows he acted badly, and he wants to make amends.'

Gracie wasn't convinced. 'He's only going to be here a few more days,' she said. 'I don't want to kiss and make up; I don't think I can face it. It's better to end it like this.'

In her head it was already over. There was nothing to be gained by trying to be friends again, only more heartache. And she'd already had enough of that to keep her going for a good long time.

—

Knowing in your head that a relationship is over and accepting it in your heart were two totally different things, Gracie brooded. As usual, she had a needle in her hand and some fabric on her lap, but what wasn't usual was that she was finding it hard to concentrate. Her mind kept presenting her with images of Lucas. The quirk of his lips, the depths in his eyes, the way his hair curled at the back of his neck. Instead of the quilt she was working on, she saw the hollow between his neck and his collarbone, the rise of his chest dipping down to his flat stomach, the trickle of hair—

Ignore it, she told herself. It was only her libido rearing its head, nothing more.

But what about his thoughtfulness? He'd taken her somewhere magical for her birthday, despite him probably being bored to death. He could have simply taken her to dinner…

Then there was his passion, and she didn't just mean in the bedroom, although that was to die for—

'Give it a rest,' she muttered. If it wasn't for passion, she wouldn't be in this mess.

But then again, she'd fallen in love with him before she'd slept with him, so she would be in this mess regardless of whether they had made love or not. Anyway, it was his passion that was the problem. If he wasn't so passionate about Under-Cover, he might have given her a chance to explain...

But wasn't his passion one of the things she loved about him? He was so focused on helping others—

There, right there, *that's* what she was having difficulty with; she couldn't continue to paint him as an utter villain when he cared so deeply for those less fortunate than himself. He didn't just *care* – he put his money where his mouth was and did something about it. Which was more than most people.

Gracie glanced down at her hands and realised she'd not sewn a stitch in twenty minutes, so with a sigh she slid her threaded needle into the fabric for safekeeping and put the quilt to one side.

Maybe he had been unreasonable and far too quick to jump to conclusions, but she had been just as quick to tell him that she never wanted to see him again; which was a total lie. She would have sold her soul for one more glimpse of the softness in his eyes as he gazed at her, if she hadn't already lost it to him. He owned her soul and her heart, and he'd be taking them with him when he left.

It didn't matter if she forgave him for what he'd done to Catrin, or that Catrin's scare hadn't actually been his fault so there was nothing to forgive – the bottom line was that Lucas was going to leave Applewell. He would be out of her life completely.

Therefore, did it matter whether they broke up today, or tomorrow, or the day after? Their break up was inevitable. She'd severed their bonds and they had to stay severed, for her own sake. She'd forgive him in her heart, even though she was still angry at him, but she'd let him continue to think she hadn't.

It was better this way; she couldn't face breaking up with him again. Once was enough.

A second time would destroy her.

Chapter 37

Lucas

'Thank you so much for babysitting this evening,' Nora said to Lucas.

'No problem, I'm happy to,' he said, chucking Ruby under the chin. The little girl stuck her tongue out at him.

'Before I go, there is one more thing,' Nora said. His normally spiky sister was looking hesitant.

'What is it?'

'It's about the wedding...' she began, and Lucas did his best not to roll his eyes. For Nora, everything was about the wedding. 'Would you give me away?'

Lucas thought he'd better sit down. 'You want *me* to give you away?'

'I should have asked before—' She stopped.

'But you didn't know whether I'd be here or not,' Lucas finished for her.

She nodded uncertainly.

'What about Dad?' Lucas hadn't really given much thought to the imminent arrival of their father. He just automatically assumed that their dad would rock up, do his duty and give Nora away, then disappear back off to Canada.

'I don't want him to do it; I want it to be you,' Nora said.

'But Dad should be the one to give you away,' Lucas insisted.

'He's hardly bothered with us for years. To be honest, I'd be surprised if he actually turns up. He'll probably come up with some excuse about his plane being delayed, or something. He didn't even come back to the UK when Ruby was born.'

He heard the subtext – that at least Lucas had managed to do that. 'I'd be honoured,' he said. 'Will my second-hand suit do, or do you think I should nip back to London and fetch my best one?'

'Your second-hand suit is fine. You look very good in it.'

'You're going to make a beautiful bride,' he said to her. She glowed and joy radiated out of her. 'Ianto is a lucky man.'

'I know,' Nora said, doing a little skip as she headed towards the door. 'Remember, Ruby's bedtime is seven o'clock. You can let her stay up till seven thirty if you really want. You've got my number if you need me. In fact, I'll probably phone you. More than once.'

Lucas shooed her away. 'Go,' he said. 'Enjoy yourself. Ruby and I will be absolutely fine, won't we, Ruby?'

Ruby nodded. She was a quiet and reserved little girl, but Lucas guessed there was an awful lot going on behind those luminous eyes.

He really enjoyed looking after his niece; not that he'd done it very often, and never on his own. The last time, Gracie had been with him. It pained him to think of it. It pained him to think of *her*. She had cut him out of her life completely, and the last time he'd spoken to her had been on the pavement outside UnderCover when she'd told him she never wanted to see him again. It seemed like she had her wish, because he hadn't seen her in Eleri's cafe, and neither had he seen her whenever he walked past A Stitch in Time.

In a moment of weakness, he'd gone to the newsagents and had stood outside reading the ads in the window, just as he had done all those weeks ago when he'd first spotted her sitting in her shop, sewing.

She hadn't been there. He knew the shop was open because the lights were on. He suspected she was hiding out the back and only emerged when the shop bell tinkled to let her know she had a customer. He debated whether to go in, but she'd made it clear she didn't want to see him.

The wedding was only three days away, three days left in Applewell. He really did want to stay, but he couldn't, not with him and Gracie the way they were. He'd debated whether to stay and fight for her, but without knowing how she truly felt about him (apart from not wanting to see him again) he didn't think handing in his notice and moving two hundred and fifty miles away from London would be the best thing for him right now. Nothing and no one would prevent him from visiting Applewell on a regular basis to see his mother, Nora and Ruby. And he might even stay for a night or two. But his dream of living in the village was dead in the water. How could it not be, when he risked bumping into the woman he loved at every turn? The pain would just be too much to bear.

He'd made a grovelling apology to Catrin, who had been in the end quite understanding, but he still felt incredibly guilty. Despite what she said, he still believed it was his fault that she'd been in danger of losing her baby. But as for Gracie, he still hadn't made his peace with her.

Ruby demanded Lucas read her a story before bed, and one story turned into three before Lucas finally managed to persuade her to snuggle down and close her eyes. He loved being with her, but he hadn't realised quite how much hard work children were, so it was with a sigh of relief that he went downstairs and rooted in the fridge for a cold beer. He popped the cap, not bothering with a glass, and went into the living room to turn the TV on. A couple of hours of mindless telly might numb his brain enough for him to stop thinking about Gracie.

There wasn't a great deal on, or should he say there wasn't a great deal he wanted to watch, so he finished his beer and decided to have one more.

It was as he got up to go to the kitchen, that he heard a faint noise from upstairs and thought it best to investigate, just in case Ruby needed a drink or the loo, or another story read to her.

He padded quietly up the stairs listening intently, wondering if she'd been calling for him, but as he drew closer to the top, he heard an odd snicking noise. Unable to work out where it was coming from, he stood on the landing and listened, his head cocked to the side.

There it was again. *Snick.*

He'd check on Ruby first, because he was pretty certain the sound wasn't coming from her bedroom, and then he'd investigate the other rooms.

But Ruby wasn't in her room. And neither was she in the bathroom.

He found her in the spare room, the bedroom where her bridesmaid's dress was hanging on a rail near the window, where Ianto's suit hung, and Nora's ballgown.

It was also the room where the wedding dress was kept.

The wedding dress was on the floor, ivory satin and lace spilling over the carpet like a puddle. Sitting next to it was Ruby, cherubic with her tousled hair and pink pyjamas, and she was holding a pair of scissors.

'*Ruby!* What are you doing?' Lucas felt sick. 'Give me the scissors, please.' They looked sharp and pointy, and very dangerous in a small child's hand.

She put them down on the carpet. 'It's OK, Uncle Lucas, I've finished.'

Gingerly he stepped forward until he was close enough to snatch them up, and once he was safely holding them he set them on top of the chest of drawers. He'd put Ruby back to bed, but first he'd hang the wedding dress back up and hide those scissors.

Carefully he lifted the wedding dress off the floor, but as he did so, he felt even sicker.

He knew exactly what Ruby had been doing with the scissors.

Nora was going to kill him.

'Ruby, what have you done?' he whispered, dread stealing over him. He wanted to cry. He hadn't seen the dress before

Ruby got her hands on it, but he was pretty sure it wasn't supposed to have great big holes in the side.

'I mended Mummy's dress,' she said, in her high lisping voice. 'Now Mummy can fit into it without eating lettuce all the time – she hates lettuce, and Daddy has to hide his chocolate because Mummy gets cross when she sees it.'

'Nora is going to kill me,' he muttered, his chest fluttering in panic. The wedding was three days away! Where the hell was Nora going to get another dress in three days? Besides which, this one was very special: it had belonged to their maternal grandmother. It was irreplaceable.

'Mummy can get a bit put in here.' Ruby pointed to the slash next to one of the seams. 'She can put a bit in from my bridesmaid's dress, like Gracie did with the baby dress for the lady, and I can wear my mermaid outfit 'cause I like it better. It's pretty and got a fishy tail.'

'What?' Lucas's brain refused to function and panic was beginning to set in.

'I'm tired now,' the little girl said, her work done for the evening.

Numbly, Lucas scooped her up and took her back to bed. He wasn't sure if he should tell her off, but he decided it would be pointless. The damage was done – literally!

As soon as Ruby was safely tucked in, Lucas retreated to the living room. What was he going to do? How could this be sorted? If it had been an off-the-peg dress, he might have stood a chance of replacing it, but this one was unique.

Oh Ruby, he thought, shaking his head. Whether she'd cut up her mother's wedding dress out of the best of intentions (so her mummy didn't have to eat lettuce) or whether she'd done so because she didn't like her bridesmaid dress and wanted to go to the wedding dressed as a mermaid was a moot point.

The only option Lucas could think of was to contact Gracie, and even that was a long shot considering the state the dress was in. He'd send her a message first, because he seriously didn't think she would answer the phone. She might have even blocked his number, which was always a possibility, but if so he'd have to find another way of contacting her.

His message was simple – *Help. Nora's wedding dress ruined.*

Hopefully that should get her attention. If he didn't hear from her within the hour, he'd have to ring Catrin, or his mother, although his mother wasn't the favoured option as she would only fret and wouldn't be able to keep it to herself either.

Lucas was harbouring the vain hope that he could whisk the dress out of the house without anyone knowing, so that Gracie could work her magic and could sneak it back in as good as new.

His phone pinged and he looked at it, his heart in his mouth. It was from Gracie.

Call me.

He took a deep breath, thankful that she hadn't blocked his number, and called her. 'I'm sorry, Gracie,' he began. 'I don't want to bother you, but Ruby has cut two big holes in Nora's wedding dress. Are you able to help?'

'I don't know until I see it. Can you bring it to me?'

'Sorry, no can do. I'm babysitting Ruby in Nora's house.'

'I'll have to come to you then, won't I?'

The phone went dead, but at least she was talking to him.

He was looking out of the window for her, and as soon as he saw her walking up the road he opened the front door and ushered her inside, his finger on his lips. 'I think Ruby is asleep,' he explained.

'Where's the dress?'

'I'll go and get it.' He crept up the stairs, taking a quick peek into Ruby's room on the way to check that she really was sound asleep, then carried the dress downstairs.

Gracie took it from him wordlessly and examined it. Her expression gave nothing away. 'What happened?'

'I put Ruby to bed, read her three stories, and thought she was asleep. Then I heard this odd noise coming from upstairs, so I went to check on her and found her cutting up her mother's wedding dress.'

'With a pair of scissors?'

'Yes. I have no idea how she got hold of them.'

'I take it she didn't hurt herself?'

'She's fine. Is there anything you can do?'

'Luckily for you, there is. For a three-year-old, Ruby is quite dextrous; she's cut right next to the seam. I may have to reinforce the material, but hopefully no one will notice.'

'Nora will.'

'Yes, she will, so you're going to have to tell her before she sees the damage for herself.'

'Couldn't you repair it first, then I'll tell her?' He looked at her hopefully.

'Do you think Ruby will stay quiet?'

Gracie had a point. The little girl had been very proud of her achievement. 'What do you mean when you say you need to put a panel in?' he asked, remembering what Ruby said about putting a bit in. 'Will you have to use Ruby's bridesmaid dress?'

'What makes you say that?'

'Ruby said she'd cut her mum's dress so that Nora wouldn't have to eat lettuce anymore, and that she could get a bit put in from her bridesmaid's dress. She mentioned that you'd done the same with a baby dress?'

Gracie looked blank. 'I'm sorry, I don't—' She paused, then said, 'Oh *yes*, I know what she means. Barbara's grandson was being christened, and the family wanted the baby to wear a christening gown that had been in the family for years. He was a rather large baby and the gown wasn't big enough, so I opened up some of the seams and put a couple of panels in. Nora and Ruby were in my shop when Barbara came to pick it up. It must have given Ruby the idea.'

Lucas had a vague memory of seeing a woman and a christening gown the first time he visited A Stitch in Time.

'How soon can you fix it?' he asked. He was still worried, but slightly more hopeful about the situation.

Gracie tapped her chin. 'What time is Nora due home?'

Lucas checked the time. 'A couple of hours, maybe three?'

'OK, this is what we'll do. You stay here with Ruby. I'm going to take this with me.' She picked up the dress. 'Two hours might be long enough. It depends on whether I've got that particular shade of ivory. I'm almost positive I have, but if I haven't, I might have to try to dye some. It's going to be tricky to get the correct shade and it may take a few goes. Are you happy for me to try to fix it?'

'Anything, do anything you possibly can. I don't care how much it costs.'

Gracie shot him a sour look. 'It's all about the money with you, isn't it?'

'No, it isn't, and if you're referring to what happened the other day, then I am truly sorry. I spoke out of turn. I shouldn't have.'

'You definitely shouldn't have. I don't want payment for this; I'm doing it out of friendship.'

Lucas watched her leave. He seemed to be doing that a lot lately.

–

'Psst!'

What was that? Lucas stood up and went out into the hall.

'Psst.'

The noise wasn't coming from upstairs, thank goodness, but from the front door. He squinted at it, and realised that the letterbox was being held open and a pair of navy eyes was staring at him through it.

'Psst,' Gracie hissed again. 'Is the coast clear?'

Lucas dashed to the door and opened it. 'Well?' he demanded.

'Is Nora back?'

'Not yet. I'm expecting her any moment, though,' he said.

'Good.' Gracie went into the living room and Lucas trailed behind. She was carrying a box, and he hoped it meant what he thought it meant.

She took it over to the table and removed the lid, then very carefully, almost reverentially, she lifted Nora's wedding dress out.

'Can I see?' he asked.

'Of course.' She held it up and he leant in for a closer look.

'You can only just about see the repair,' he said wonder in his voice. He gazed at her, then back at the dress. 'I can't thank you enough.'

'You still need to tell Nora, because Ruby will even if you don't,' Gracie advised.

He was about to take the dress back upstairs when the front door opened. Nora was giggling quietly at something while trying to tell Ianto to shush. She looked surprised when she saw Gracie.

'Hello, Gracie, I didn't expect to see you here.' Nora was well aware of what had happened between Lucas and Gracie, and between him and Catrin. He didn't think there was anyone in the village who didn't know. She gave him and Gracie a curious look, then her gaze sharpened as it came to rest on her wedding dress. 'Why is that down here?'

'Don't panic,' Lucas said, and he immediately saw the panic in her eyes. 'There's been a bit of an incident.'

Nora whirled around and was about to rush up the stairs to check on Ruby, when Lucas said, 'Ruby is fine. It's your dress that isn't, or rather, wasn't. Gracie came to the rescue.'

'What are you talking about?' Nora demanded. She was frowning heavily and staring at the dress.

'Somehow, and don't ask me how because I've no idea, Ruby got hold of a pair of scissors, and she decided to... um...'

'...let your dress out,' Gracie explained.

'Bless her,' Lucas said. 'She was only thinking of you. She said she didn't want to see you eat lettuce anymore because you didn't like it.'

'Wait, are you telling me that Ruby got hold of a pair of scissors and she did something to my dress?'

'That's exactly what I'm telling you.' Lucas winced. 'But Gracie has repaired it. You'd never know.'

Nora's voice was cold. 'Give it to me. Let me see.'

Wordlessly Gracie handed it to her, and Lucas held his breath while Nora examined it.

For a very long time she didn't say anything, but when she looked up, she was smiling. Lucas let out his breath in a rush, relief making his knees go weak.

'This repair is marvellous,' she said to Gracie, 'but I've got some bad news for you.'

Gracie licked her lips nervously and her eyes widened. 'What?' she asked cautiously.

'I was actually going to ask you to let it out, because there's no way I'm going to reach my target weight.' She ran her finger down the almost invisible repair.

'You want me to *let it out*?' Gracie asked.

'If it's not too much trouble,' Nora said.

Gracie rolled her eyes. 'It's definitely not too much trouble. Do I have to let your prom dress out as well?'

'I think you'll have to, maybe quite a bit.'

Lucas blinked. What did Nora mean?

Gracie cottoned on faster than he did. 'Are you pregnant?' she asked.

Nora nodded, grinning.

'Congratulations,' Gracie cried, before Lucas had a chance to say anything. He was still trying to gather his thoughts. Gosh! He was going to be an uncle again. How absolutely marvellous!

'Does Mum know?' he asked his sister.

'No, and I don't want you to tell her. There will be time enough after the honeymoon. I only mentioned it now because

I need Gracie to let the wedding dress out. Gracie, I'm so sorry I waited until the last minute; I was going to call on you in the morning. Thank goodness the wedding is only three days away, otherwise I think you might have had to let it out even more.'

'Come and see me tomorrow and I'll take some measurements.' Gracie yawned. 'I'd better get off home.'

'Let me walk you,' Lucas offered.

'No thanks, I can manage. I'll be fine on my own.'

Nora said, 'Gracie, let him walk you home, please. I know Applewell is as safe as houses but it would put my mind at rest to know he'd made sure you got home safely.'

Lucas walked to the door, Gracie ahead of him. When he reached it, he turned and mouthed, 'Thank you,' to his sister. She smiled and he just about made out the words 'You're welcome.'

Gracie had started speaking to him again, albeit in stilted sentences and with a cross look on her face, but he now had an opportunity to make things up to her and he didn't intend to waste it. He was going to tell Gracie he loved her and that he wanted to stay in Applewell for good.

Whether he actually did so would be up to her...

Chapter 38

Gracie

'Thank you,' Lucas said to her as soon as he closed Nora's front door. Gracie felt his light touch on her arm and she shrugged him off. There was no way she was going to be his booty call for the evening; she had three days to endure before he left, and she had to stay strong.

'I've got something to say to you,' Lucas persisted. 'Will you listen?'

'If you're going to apologise again, you've already said it about six times.'

'I'm not going to apologise again,' he said. 'Either you accept it, or you don't. I hope you know I didn't mean what I said, and realise it was coming from a place of concern for UnderCover.'

Gracie didn't care where it was coming from. 'You should have trusted me.'

'You're right, I should have.'

'Then we've really nothing to say to each other, have we?' She was staring stonily ahead, wishing Nora hadn't been so insistent that he walked her home. She'd been walking the streets of Applewell since she was a child. Nothing had happened to her then, and nothing would happen to her now.

'I'm not going back to London,' he said.

Gracie stumbled, and his arm shot out to steady her. 'I'm sorry, what did you say?' she asked.

'I said, I'm not going back to London. I'm staying in Applewell.'

Gracie's heart squeezed so hard, she thought she might pass out. Surely he wasn't serious? The only thing that had been keeping her going was the fact that she wouldn't have to see him again after the weekend. Yet here he was telling her that she'd see his face almost every day. There would be no escape.

She knew the heartache was going to stay with her for a very long time indeed, but now it would stab her in the chest every time she saw him, every time she heard his name spoken, every time she heard his voice.

That would teach her to fall in love. Had she any inkling of what she was letting herself in for, she would have run a mile the first time she saw him.

'Are you sure that's what you want?' she asked, trying to keep her voice level and not let him see how badly the news was affecting her. 'What about UnderCover?'

'It'll go on without me. I've done what I can for the charity; I can't do any more, not without returning to my old job.'

'What are you going to do in Applewell?'

'I have absolutely no idea. I'm sure something will turn up.'

'Where are you going to live?' She felt as though she was asking loads of questions.

'I've got to sort my flat out. I haven't decided whether to rent it out or sell it.'

Gracie took a steadying breath. 'At least if you rent it out, you can always go back to it when you want to.'

'Yes, that's a point. I hadn't thought of that. I'll have to sell it then. I want to make a clean break. I don't want to give myself a get-out clause.'

'Why? Do you think you're going to need one?'

A look of pain flitted across his face. 'I hope not. It all depends on you.'

'On *me*? How do you figure that out?'

'Because I love you.'

Wait, what! Had she heard him properly? 'You love me?' she repeated woodenly, convinced she must have heard him incorrectly.

'Yes, I do.'

'You've only known me for a couple of months.'

'Does it matter? I won't know you at all if I move back to London.'

Her heart was skipping so many beats, she thought she might faint. He *loved* her. She didn't believe it. How could a worldly-wise handsome man like him love someone like her? He must be making it up. Surely it was an attempt to get into her knickers again for one last fling before he went back to London and forgot about her.

'You don't believe me, do you?' he said.

Mutely she shook her head. It wasn't possible. It was some sick joke he was playing, and she didn't appreciate it.

'Right, I'll prove it.' He got his phone out of his pocket, and a second later she could hear the faint noise of a ringtone.

'Who are you calling? Do you realise how late it is?'

'I don't care. Oh, hi, Jonas, so sorry it's late but it couldn't wait. I'm going to put you on speaker.' Lucas fumbled with his phone for a second, then held it up between them. 'I've got someone with me,' he said, 'and I want her to hear this because otherwise she won't believe me.'

'Lucas, it's gone eleven.' Jonas's voice was tinny.

'I know and I'm sorry, but as I said, this can't wait.' Lucas turned to Gracie so he could look her in the eye. Mesmerised, Gracie was unable to look away. 'I'm handing in my resignation,' Lucas said. 'I believe my notice period is four weeks?'

'I must say, this is very sudden,' Jonah said, after a pause. 'What brought this on?'

'I'm in love,' Lucas said, 'and if I come back to London I'll lose her.' His eyes bored into hers and Gracie felt herself sinking.

'What about UnderCover? Are you just going to walk away?'

Lucas blinked slowly. 'I have to; I can't come back to London,' he repeated.

'Have you thought this through? You're throwing away a promising career.'

'I'm not throwing anything away,' Lucas said. 'I'm hoping to gain something – the woman I love.'

'Look,' Jonas reasoned. 'Take a few days to think it over. And I mean a proper think, not just a knee-jerk reaction.'

'No, thank you, I've made up my mind. I'm leaving four weeks from today. I'm sorry, Jonas, I know that's not what you want to hear and I can't thank you enough for keeping my job open for me, but Angel will be fine, and UnderCover will be fine. Of course I'll continue to support the charity in any way I can, just not in a formal capacity.'

'If that's your decision, I wish you well. If you need a reference, I'll give you a glowing one,' Jonas said, 'and I don't expect you back in the office. You can wind up what you're doing for the website, and we'll call it quits.'

'That's very generous of you,' Lucas said. He swallowed, and Gracie knew how much this was costing him. She tugged at his arm.

'Hang on a sec.' Lucas put his hand over the microphone. 'What is it?' he asked her.

'Don't do this just for me, Lucas. You'll regret it.'

He inhaled sharply. 'Because you don't feel the same way?'

'That's not it at all. But UnderCover is your life. I don't know even a fraction of your story, but I can tell how much the charity means to you. You can't just walk away.'

'I want to. I want you more than I want anything else, and if it means walking away from my job and my life in the city, then so be it. I'm happy here. I know I've only been in Applewell a couple of months, but it's home. It *finally* feels like home.'

Gracie felt the prickle of tears behind her eyes. Lucas meant it, really meant it.

She waited for him to finish his conversation with Jonas, not listening in, but thinking of those three little words, and when the call ended and his attention was wholly and utterly on her, she said those three words back to him.

'I love you.' Her voice was little more than a whisper, but his smile told her he'd heard her loud and clear. And the way he kissed her, and the depth of love in his eyes, told her that he was absolutely thrilled about it.

Epilogue

Lucas

'You want me to do *what*?' Lucas sat down, the phone glued to his ear. He was having trouble making sense of what Jonas was saying.

'Manage the shop in Applewell,' Jonas repeated. 'I've received a notification that the current manager is pregnant and won't be taking up her position after her maternity leave.'

'Do you mean Catrin?' Lucas asked.

'That's right. She will be starting her maternity leave in four months, so I'd like to offer you the job if you want it.'

Lucas was serving the last day of his notice period and he'd assumed Jonas was calling to wish him all the best. He needed it, too, not yet having secured another job, although he had a few irons in the fire.

'Of course, it's considerably less than you were on…' Jonas added.

'I'll take it.' Silently he fist-pumped the air. He'd got a job! And not just any old job; it was a job he'd come to love in the three months since he'd begun helping out in the shop.

'It might be an idea for you to start working there now, so there's no break in your employment,' Jonas suggested, and Lucas knew the man didn't have to offer him that. UnderCover would be paying two salaries for the same position, which it could ill afford to do.

'That's not necessary,' Lucas protested. He had enough savings (just) to keep himself afloat until Catrin began her maternity leave.

'I insist,' Jonas said. 'I'm not doing this out of the goodness of my heart; I want you to set up training courses for branch managers in how to identify designer labels and vintage items, and I also want you to write a set of procedures. That should keep you out of mischief for a while.'

'Gosh…' Lucas was astounded and immensely grateful, and he couldn't wait to share the news with Gracie and the rest of his family.

This called for a celebration, and he knew just what he was going to do.

Gracie

'Close your eyes,' Lucas told her, and Gracie closed them. The path down to the cove was levelling out the nearer they got to the beach, but nevertheless Gracie was concerned she might slip and fall, so she clung tightly to Lucas's hands as he guided her down the last little bit and out onto the sand.

She felt her feet sinking into it and she wondered at all the secrecy. She'd been to the cove more times than she cared to remember – it was hardly going to be a surprise – but Lucas had been like a dog with two tails all day, so she was happy to go along with it. Her trust in him was absolute and she knew he wouldn't let her down.

'OK, you can open them,' he instructed, and she gasped at the sight in front of her.

Above the high tide mark was a table and two chairs. The table had been laid with a white cloth and gleaming cutlery. In the centre sat a storm lantern with a candle flickering inside it. A small barbeque had been set up to one side, and smoke spiralled into the air from the hot coals. A cool box was next to it.

'What's this for?' she asked.

'I've got a job.'

'That's brilliant news! Well done!' She gave him a smacker of a kiss, thrilled for him. 'Who will you be working for?'

'UnderCover.'

Gracie hesitated. 'Isn't this supposed to be your last day working for them?' A coldness was creeping along her veins and heading for her heart. What did he mean?

'It is, but Jonas phoned me this morning and offered me a position I simply couldn't turn down.'

Gracie swallowed convulsively as her thoughts raced. Then she inhaled deeply and let the worry go: Lucas would never do anything to hurt her. 'Tell me more,' she urged.

He pulled the seat out for her and she sat down, the chair legs sinking a little in the sand. Lucas opened the wine with a pop and poured her a glass. Gracie took a sip. It was cool and fruity.

'Catrin is going on maternity leave in four months,' he said, and Gracie nodded. She knew this. Her friend's pregnancy was starting to show now, and her tummy was becoming quite round.

'She doesn't intend to go back to work after the baby is born, and Jonas wants me to manage the shop,' Lucas told her.

Gracie hadn't thought that far ahead, but it looked like Catrin had. Then she grinned. 'What a perfect solution,' she declared.

'It's less money,' he said.

'Does that bother you?'

'Not at all. Money isn't everything.'

'Unless it's for UnderCover,' Gracie joked, and Lucas laughed.

'You're never going to let me forget that, are you?'

'This is lovely, but why are we dining on the beach?' she asked.

'Because I can't afford to fly you to America for a $5000 burger, so a supermarket special cooked on the beach is the next best thing.'

'Who wants a burger that costs that much anyway?' she asked.

'If I remember rightly, you certainly didn't when I told you about it. In fact, you were quite scandalised. I didn't realise it at the time, but that was when I fell in love with you.'

'Shall we skip the burger, for now? I haven't been kissed for at least half an hour,' Gracie suggested. The food could wait. She wanted to feel his lips on hers and his arms around her, because that was the only thing that mattered.

And when his mouth claimed hers, she knew that in the patchwork quilt of life, love was the stitches that held it together, and she couldn't wait to see how all their pieces looked and what brilliant new pattern they would make.